ESPEN ASH LAD

Folk Tales from Norway

Espen Ash Lad, by Erik Werenskiold.
Illustration © O. Væring Eftf. AS.

ESPEN ASH LAD

Folk Tales from Norway

translated by Robert Gambles

HAYLOFT PUBLISHING LTD
CUMBRIA

First published by Hayloft Publishing Ltd., 2014

Hayloft Publishing Ltd, South Stainmore,
Kirkby Stephen, Cumbria, CA17 4DJ

tel: 017683 41568 or 07971 352473
email: books@hayloft.eu
web: www.hayloft.eu

ISBN 978 1 910237 045

A CIP catalogue record for this book is available from the British Library

Designed, printed and bound in the EU

Papers used by Hayloft are natural, recyclable products made from wood grown
in sustainable forests. The manufacturing processes conform to the
environmental regulations of the country of origin.

from the collected stories of
Peter Christen Asbjørnsen and Jørgen Moe

translated from the Norwegian by Robert Gambles
in memory of my wife, Hannemor,
whose love made everything possible

Notes

The tales are presented in the order given by Peter Asbjørnsen and Jørgen Moe. The tale of Soria Moria Castle has been included because its principal character, Halvor, so closely resembles Ash Lad and because the story itself encapsulates the spirit and values depicted in the other stories. It also holds a special place in the affections of the Norwegian people.

I also wish to acknowledge the guidance offered by the work of the publishers, editors and translators of the many versions of the Asbjørnsen and Moe stories which have appeared over the past 160 years, as the structure of the Norwegian language has evolved.

I should like especially to thank my publisher, Dawn Robertson, at Hayloft Publishing for her enthusiastic support and encouragement at all stages in the preparation of this book.

Contents

Almost all the images used in this book came from O.Væring which is one of Norway's oldest and largest photographic agencies within the field of Norwegian and some international art.

This photographic archive is from the end of the 19th century. From this period photographers through the years have photographed the artist's original production.

All art images – old and new – in the archive of O.Væring will forever be just as appropriate for use in books and other media – they are an unique artistic and cultural treasure.

The author and publisher wish to give particular thanks to Ingrid Petersson for all her help with these wonderful illustrations.

Illustrations

Introduction

In May 1814, just 200 years ago, Norway took an historic step towards national independence after many centuries of domination by Denmark. One hundred and twelve representatives from all sections of society met in a country house at Eidsvoll, some fifty kilometres north of Oslo, and agreed on a detailed permanent constitution based broadly on the principles enshrined in the French Revolutionary Constitution of 1791, the American Declaration of Independence and the British system of government. Most significantly of all it declared that Norway was a "free, independent and indivisible realm" governed by a limited monarchy. This brave defiance of the recent Treaty of Kiel by which Norway was awarded to its belligerent neighbour, Sweden, met with the disapproval of the great powers of Europe, and a Swedish invasion quickly put an end to Norway's immediate aspirations of independent state-hood.

The general sentiment in Europe at the time was that Norway did not possess any of the attributes which go to make a nation: it had no independent history, no social cohesion, no established system of government or law, no recognisable heritage of cultural achievement, no place on the international stage. In the century that followed Norway was decisively to prove otherwise. In 1905, amid much diplomatic and political confusion and Swedish reluctance, the union with Sweden was finally ended and Norway became a fully sovereign nation with Prince Carl of Denmark as its king (a choice overwhelmingly confirmed by popular referendum) and Princess Maud, the daughter of the British King, Edward VII, as its Queen.

By the early 20th century most of the capital cities of Europe were talking of the great plays of Henrik Ibsen and the new National Theatre in Oslo; listening to the music of Edvard Grieg, Johan Halvorsen and Johan Svendsen; ardently discussing the paintings of Edvard Munch; reading the novels of Knut Hamsun; acknowledging the literary genius of Bjørnstjerne Bjørnson who, in 1903, was awarded the Nobel prize for literature; following the exploits of Norwegian explorers such as Roald Amundsen and Fridtjof Nansen; admiring the achievements of the latter in the world of diplomacy, international relations and humanitarian missions; and taking note of the historical scholarship of the many volumes of Peter Munch's *History of the Norwegian People*. And in all these years Norway had been developing its mercantile marine and its international economic status until it ranked among the most important in the world.

All this encouraged European (and American) awareness of Norway as a nation in its own right and this was also enhanced by Alfred Nobel's choice of the Norwegian Parliament as the body to award his Peace Prize, and, perhaps even more, by the discovery of Norway as an exciting destination for tourists as every year the steamers brought thousands of visitors from other countries to marvel at the fjord and mountain scenery and to fish in its salmon-rich waters; and, for many, to note the virtues of a new form of social and political democracy. Of immense significance, too, was the composition and official recognition of the Norwegian National Anthem, first ceremonially sung on 17 May 1864, the 50th anniversary of the signing of the Eidsvoll Constitution and Declaration of Independence.

Among the first of all the strands which drew together to create a wider awareness of Norway's separate identity, and, within Norway, a strong sense of nationhood, was the publication in 1852 of *Norwegian Folk Tales*, the product of ten years' work in the rural communities of southern, eastern and western Norway by Peter Christen Asbjørnsen and Jørgen Moe. Inspired by the success of the Brothers Grimm in Germany, they had revealed in the remote valleys and high mountains a rich and original vein of Norwegian literature such as had not been seen since the age of the Sagas; and the authors had aimed to present the tales in a distinctively Norwegian (i.e. non-Danish) language. It was not only in Norway that this collection of folk tales was received with acclamation: in Germany, for example, they were regarded as master-pieces of folk literature and Jacob Grimm commented that they had 'a freshness and fullness which surpass nearly all others'; and in Britain a translation, published in 1859, by Sir George Dasent proved immensely popular, while a selection for children became a classic, and not only in Britain.

To understand and appreciate these folk tales one should try to imagine what life was like in earlier centuries in the remote valleys of Norway. Dasent considered the dales folk to be 'among the most primitive examples left of peasant life'. Families of several generations – grandparents, parents, children and perhaps great-grandchildren – lived on small farmsteads, often some distance from their nearest neighbours, surrounded by deep, dark spruce forests and high mountains or moorland.

They rarely travelled beyond their own valleys and had to be self-sufficient, producing their own food from livestock, field and forest; spinning, weaving and making their own clothing; cutting timber for fuel, furniture, household utensils, farm implements, byres and the very house they lived in;

seeking in herbal concoctions the medical remedies they so often needed; and enduring each year many months of hard northern winter and long dark nights. They were conventionally Christian and were conscientious in religious observance and attendance at church but folk memory of pagan customs and superstitions was still strong as was a belief in magic and the supernatural.

There are many references to 'kings' in these stories who lived in palatial luxury, administered cruel and arbitrary punishments and held the power of life and death over lesser men. These were not kings as we know them but local landowners, nor were their houses 'palaces' as we know them but rather substantial farmhouses or manors. The 'princesses' of the stories were, of course, the daughters of these wealthy farmers. Erik Werenskiold researching for his famous illustrations to the folk tales in 19th century Gudbrandsdal, wrote that 'on the great farms there were small kings and the tenant farmers were their serfs... One could sense the Middle Ages and behind the great forest lay the Troll world of the Jotunheim mountains. I have never since found anything that seemed more Norwegian.'

The church provided moral guidance but superstition and inherited beliefs in the supernatural inevitably flourished in such an isolated environment where life was dominated by the forces of unpredictable nature. It is not surprising that so many of the folk tales refer to the poverty of these peasant farmers and to their dreams of a life of wealth and plenty but, even so, the great occasions of life – birth, death and especially weddings – were celebrated with traditional feasting and ceremony. Nor is it surprising that the misfortunes of life were explained by the hostile or mischievous interference in human affairs by supernatural beings: fairies, elves and dwarfs feature in most European folk literature – only Scandinavia has trolls, often giants, who inhabit caves in the mountains and carry off women and children and inflict disaster on crops and livestock.

Magic, too, played its part in the fantasies of achieving a better life which were the theme of tales told during the dark days of autumn and winter: spells could be broken and problems solved by a magic flute or key-ring or the ability to hear the grass growing a thousand miles away. But equally important in these tales is the success that can be achieved by the ability of the human brain to solve problems by analysing the difficulties, working out a solution, preparing a plan of action, acquiring any necessary equipment, and by courageous quick-thinking and decisive action as the task unfolds, and by showing kindness to others and especially to those in need. Courage, modesty, endurance and native ability are to be admired and will bring their reward.

Asbjørnsen and Moe (and Moe's son, Moltke) made several collections of Norwegian folk tales comprising 110 in all, fourteen of which are included in this selection and are known as the tales of Espen Askeladd, the Ash Lad, the youngest of three brothers who is constantly mocked and looked down upon as lazy, incapable and fit for nothing except to attend to the more tedious household chores and to sit in the hearth and poke among the embers – the ash boy, Cinderella's 'brother'.

Yet when it comes to actual achievement in solving a problem it is he who is shown to be capable of analytical and imaginative thinking, tactical planning, quick-thinking and with the ability to outwit trolls as well as more earthly adversaries. It is he who succeeds and wins the princess and half the kingdom where his more conventional, unimaginative, macho brothers always fail. In Norway and throughout much of the western world he became a folk hero, the little man who always wins through when bigger men fall by the wayside.

The text of the tales was famously accompanied by illustrations drawn by several of the many Norwegian artists whose work was widely admired in the late 19th century, notably Theodor Kittelsen, Erik Werenskiold and Otto Sinding. These illustrations had a special appeal to children and helped to make the tales a childrens' classic in Norway and far beyond.

There have been several selective translations of these stories into the English language, with varying degrees of success, but, as far as I am aware, there has never been an exclusive collection of the Askeladd tales. The author of these translations has aimed to keep as closely as possible to the original text while presenting the stories in modern English idiom.

I acknowledge with gratitude the help given to me in the preparation of this book by Eva von Heyden and Randi Farbrot in Oslo, and I dedicate it to the memory of my wife, Hannemor, who first introduced me to these stories.

A 'king', by Erik Werenskiold.
Illustration © O. Væring Eftf. AS.

Ash Lad who stole the troll's silver ducks

Once upon a time there was a poor man who had three sons. When he died the two older sons went out into the world to try their luck but the youngest, Espen Ash Lad, they wouldn't have with them at any price.

"As for you," they said, "you're good for nothing except to poke about in the ashes."

"In that case," said Ash Lad, "I'll go by myself, that's what I'll do."

The two set off and arrived at the king's manor where they obtained employment – one with the Master of the Horse and the other with the gardener. Ash Lad too set off taking with him a big, heavy bread-kneading trough which was the only possession left by his parents but the other two could not be bothered with that. The trough was heavy to carry but Ash Lad didn't want to leave it behind.

After he had gone some distance he too arrived at the king's manor and asked for employment. They told him that they had no use for him but he asked so very courteously that in the end he was allowed to be in the kitchen and carry in wood and water for the kitchen maid. He worked hard and quickly and it wasn't long before everyone became fond of him. But the other two were lazy and received more blows than rewards and they became envious of Ash Lad when they saw how much better he was treated than they were.

Right opposite the king's manor, on the other side of a large lake, there lived a troll who had seven silver ducks which

17

swam on the lake and so could be seen from the king's manor. The king had often wished to have these ducks for himself and so the two brothers said to the Master of the Horse:

"Our brother has said that, if he chose, he could easily get those seven silver ducks for the king."

You can imagine that it was not long before the Master of Horse mentioned this to the king; and so the king summoned Ash Lad to him and said: "Your brothers tell me that you can catch those silver ducks for me, so now go and do it."

"I have never thought or said such a thing," said Ash Lad.

But the king insisted: "You have said you can do this, so now you must go and do it."

"Well then," said Ash Lad, "Since I have no option, if I can have a sack of rye and a sack of wheat, I'll see what I can do."

He got what he asked for and put it in the trough he had brought from home and rowed across the lake with it. When he reached the other side he walked along the shore scattering the grain and in the end he enticed the ducks into the trough and rowed back as fast as he could, but when he was out in the middle of the lake the troll spotted him.

"Hi you!" the troll shouted, "Have you gone off with my seven silver ducks?"

"Yes, I have," called Ash Lad.

"And are you planning to come again?" asked the troll.

"I might," replied the lad.

When he came back to the king with the seven silver ducks he was more popular than before, and even the king said he had done well. But his brothers became even more annoyed and envious and in the end they went to the Master of the Horse and told him that Ash Lad had said that, if he chose, he could get the king the troll's bed-quilt with its gold and silver quilted patches.

"Have you gone off with my seven silver ducks?" by Theodor Kittelsen. Illustration © O. Væring Eftf. AS.

The Master of the Horse was not slow this time in telling the king about this, and the king told the lad that his brothers said that he had said he could get hold of the troll's bed-quilt with its silver and gold patches, so now he must go and do it – or lose his life. Ash Lad replied that he had never thought or said such a thing, but that didn't help him so he asked for three days to make his plans.

When the three days had gone by, he rowed over the lake in his trough and walked around spying out the land. At last he noticed that folk in the troll's mountain cave came to hang out the bed-quilt to air, and when they had gone back inside the mountain Ash Lad grabbed it and rowed back as fast as he could. When he was half-way across out came the troll and spotted him and shouted "Hi you! Are you the one who took my seven silver ducks?"

"Yes, that's me," said Espen.

"And now have you taken my bed-quilt with the silver and gold patches as well?"

"Yes, I have," said Ash Lad.

"And are you planning to come many more times?"

"I might," said Ash Lad.

When he came back to the king with the bed-quilt with its gold and silver patchwork everyone thought more highly of him than ever and he was given employment in the king's household itself. This made the other two even more annoyed and to get their revenge they hit on the idea of telling the Master of Horse that their brother had boasted that he could get the king the troll's golden harp which was so beautiful to hear that everyone who heard it felt happy – no matter how sad they were before.

So the Master of Horse went straight to the king to tell him, and the king said to Ash Lad: "If you have said this, then you must do it. If you succeed, then you shall have the Princess and half the kingdom, but if you fail you will lose your life."

Ash Lad replied, "I have never thought or said such a thing, but it seems there is no way out of it so I might as well try. I would like six days to make preparations."

The king agreed that he could have six days but after that he must be on his way.

So, he put in his pocket a nail, a birch-wood peg, and a candle-stub and rowed across. He walked furtively to and fro outside the troll's mountain cave and after a while the troll came out and saw him.

"Are you the one who stole my seven silver ducks?" he shouted.

"Yes, that was me," said Espen.

"And are you the one who took my bed-quilt with the gold and silver patches?" the troll asked.

"Yes, that was me," Ash Lad said.

So the troll grabbed hold of him and took him into the cave in the mountain.

"Now, my dear daughter," he said, "I've caught the one who took my silver ducks and my bed-quilt with the gold and silver patches. Put him in the pen and feed him well and then we'll kill him and invite the whole family to a feast."

She was only too willing to do this and she put him in the pen without delay, and there he remained for eight days and was fed on the finest food and drink he could wish for.

Then, when eight days had passed the troll told his daughter to go down and make a cut in his little finger so that she could see if he was fat enough. She went down to the pen and said "Hold out your little finger." But Ash Lad held out the nail he had brought and she cut into that.

"Oh no," said the troll's daughter when she came back to her father. "He's still as hard as iron. He is not ready to eat yet."

After another eight days the same thing happened, the only difference being that this time Ash Lad held out the birch peg.

"He's a little better," she said when she came back to the troll, "but he's still as hard as wood to chew."

Eight days later the troll told his daughter to go down to see if he was fat enough yet.

"Hold out your little finger," said the troll's daughter to the lad in the pen.

This time Ash Lad held out the candle-end.

"Now he'll do well enough," she said.

"That's fine," said the troll. "Now we'll set off and invite the guests. Meanwhile, you must kill him and roast one half of him and boil the other half.

So when the troll was well on his way his daughter began to sharpen a great long knife.

"Is that what you are going to kill me with?" asked the lad.

"Yes, that's right," said the troll's daughter.

"But it isn't sharp enough," said Ash Lad. "Let me sharpen it for you and then you can kill me much more easily."

So, she let him have the knife and he set to, honing and sharpening it.

Then he said, "Let me try it out on one of your hair plaits. I think it should be sharp enough now,"

He was given permission to do this but at the same moment as he grasped the hair plait he pulled her head back and cut off her head. Half of her he roasted and half of her he boiled and set it out on the table. He then dressed himself in her clothes and sat himself down in the corner.

When the troll came home with his guests he told his daughter – for he thought it was his daughter who sat there –

that she too should come and eat.

"No, I won't have anything to eat," answered Ash Lad, "I feel so tired and out of sorts."

"Oh well, you know the cure for that," said the troll, "take the harp and play it."

"Yes, but where is it?" asked Ash Lad.

"You know very well where it is," said the troll. "You used it last. It's hanging over there by the door, of course."

The lad didn't wait to be told twice. He took the gold harp and strolled about in and out of the house making music, but all at once he pushed off in the trough and rowed away so fast that the spray flew around.

After a while the troll thought his daughter had been absent a long time and he went out to see what had happened to her. It was then he spotted the lad in the trough far, far out on the lake.

"Hey, you!" he shouted, "Are you the one who took my seven silver ducks?"

"Yes," agreed Ash Lad.

"And now have you taken my golden harp?" the troll roared.

"Yes, I certainly have," said Espen Ash Lad.

"And haven't I eaten you up after all then?"

"No, it was your own daughter you ate," the lad replied.

When the troll heard that, he was so furious that he burst. So Ash Lad rowed back again and took a whole heap of gold and silver – as much as the trough could carry. Then when he arrived at the king's manor with the golden harp he got the princess and half the kingdom just as the king had promised him. He was generous towards his brothers as he thought they had only wished him well when they had spoken as they did.

The Princess who had to have the last word

Once upon a time there was a king who had a daughter who was so wilful and who talked so much that no-one was able to get her to hold her tongue. So the king declared that the man who could make her keep silent would have the princess and half the kingdom as well.

As you can imagine, there were plenty who were keen to try, for it is not every day that one can get a king's daughter and half a kingdom for almost nothing. The gate to the king's manor was constantly open; they came in flocks and droves, from east and west, some riding and some on foot. But not one of them could get the princess to stop talking. In the end the king declared that those who tried but were unsuccessful should be branded on both ears with his great branding iron; he was not prepared to have all this coming and going through his manor to no purpose.

Now there were three brothers who had heard of this princess and, since there was nothing in the world to keep them at home, they made up their minds to try their luck and see if they could win the king's daughter and half the king-dom. All three of them went together.

When they had travelled some distance on their way, the youngest of the three, Espen Ash Lad, found a dead magpie.

"Look what I've found!" he called, "Look what I've found!"

"What's that you've found?" his brothers asked.

"I've found a dead magpie," he said.

"Pshaw! Throw it away! What's the use of that?" said the

other two who always considered themselves to be so clever.

"Ah well," said Espen, "I've nothing much to do and nothing much to carry, so I might as well take it with me."

When they had gone a little further Espen Ash Lad found an old wicker ring woven from thin osier twigs. He picked it up.

"Look what I've found!" he called, "Look what I've found!"

"Now what have you found?" said his brothers.

"I've found a wicker ring," he replied.

"Pshaw! What use is that? Throw it away!" they said.

"I've nothing much to do and nothing much to carry, so I might as well take it along," said Ash Lad.

When they had gone a little further, he found a piece of a broken dish and he picked this up too.

"Hey, guys!" he cried, "Look what I've found! Look what I've found!"

"Well, what have you found now?" his brothers asked.

"A piece of a broken dish," he said.

"Pish! That really is something to take with us! Just drop it!" they said.

"Oh, I've nothing much to do and not much to carry," said Ash Lad, "so I might as well take it along."

When they had gone a little further he found a crooked ram's horn and soon afterwards he found another exactly like it.

"Look what I've found!" he shouted. "Look what I've found!"

"What have you found, now?" the others asked.

"Two ram's horns," Ash Lad replied.

"Oh Pish!" they said, "What use are they? Throw them away!"

"No," said Espen, "I've nothing much to do and not much to carry, so I'll take them along."

A short while later he found an iron wedge, the kind used

'"Good day to you," she said,' by Erik Werenskiold.
Illustration © O. Væring Eftf. AS.

to split tough logs.

"Look what I've found!" he shouted. "Look what I've found!"

"It's a mighty lot of finding you are doing," said the other two. "What is it you've found this time?"

"I've found an iron wedge," he answered.

"Oh! Throw it away! What use have we got for that?" they said.

"I've nothing much to do and not much to carry, so I'll just take it along," said Ash Lad.

When they were walking near to the king's manor – across fields where manure had just been spread – Espen Ash Lad bent down and picked up a worn-out shoe sole.

"Just look what I've found now!" he said. "Look what I've found!"

"If you would only find a little common sense before you get there..." said the other two. "What is it you've found this time?"

"A worn-out shoe-sole," he replied.

"Oh! That's something fantastic to pick up! Throw it away! What use is that to you?" his brothers said.

"Ah well!," said Ash Lad, "I've nothing much to do and not much to carry, so I might as well take it along if I'm going to win the princess and half the kingdom."

"Oh yes! You're the one most likely to do that!" said the other two.

And so they were allowed to meet the king's daughter. The eldest went in first.

"Good day," he said

"Good day to you," she replied curtly.

"It's terribly hot in here," he said.

"It's much hotter in the fire," answered the princess.

The branding iron lay waiting. When he saw that, he had no

Norwegian wicker ring, 'vidjespenning',
copyright Norsk Skogmuseum, Elverum.

more to say, and so that was the end of him.

Things went no better for the next one:

"Good day," he said.

"Good day to you," she said, turning her back on him.

"It's terribly hot in here," he said.

"It's much hotter in the fire," she replied.

Hearing that, he lost his voice and couldn't speak, so out came the branding iron again.

Then it was Ash Lad's turn. "Good day," he said.

"Good day to you," she replied curtly, turning away.

"It's nice and warm in here," said Espen Ash Lad.

"It's warmer in the fire," she replied. The arrival of the third brother had not made her temper any sweeter.

"Perhaps it would be a good idea to roast my magpie there then?" he asked.

"I'm afraid it would burst," said the king's daughter.

"Oh, that won't be a problem," the boy replied. "I'll just tie this wicker ring* round the magpie."

"It's too big," she said.

"In that case I'll push in a wedge," said Ash Lad and he brought out the wedge.

"The fat will drip off her," said the king's daughter.

"Then I'll just hold this underneath," the boy replied, producing the broken dish.

"You certainly know how to twist words," said the princess.

"No, I'm not twisted. But this really is twisted," Espen replied, and took out one of the ram's horns.

"Goodness, I've never see anything like that!" the princess cried.

"Well, here's one exactly like it!" said Ash Lad, taking out the other one.

"I think you are determined to wear me out and have the last word, aren't you?" she said.

"No, you are not worn out but this certainly is," said Ash Lad, and took out the shoe-sole.

And the princess had nothing more to say.

"Now you are mine," said Espen Ash Lad. And so he won her and half the kingdom as well.

---

*A wicker ring was an item with many uses and was in everyday use in Norway for centuries. It was made from willow wands or, preferably, from the roots of the birch tree which were stronger, woven together in the form of a ring of whatever size was required. The ends were woven to form a small ring and a hook to act as a fastening. They had multiple uses in the home and on the farm: as a general purpose hanger, as a gate fastener, to tether animals, to secure loads on carts or sledges, to hold together any items as we would use string or rope, or, as Ash Lad proposed, to keep a roast intact during cooking. They are now made as objets d'art or souvenirs.

Ash Lad has an Eating Contest
with a Troll*

There was once a farmer who had three sons. He was old and weak and not at all well off, and his sons were idle and unwilling to lend him a hand. The farm owned a fine large woodland and the father wanted his sons to go and cut timber there to try to pay off some of his debts.

At long last he persuaded them to set off from the farm. The eldest was to be the first to go to cut the timber but when he had gone deep into the wood and began to chop at a moss-grown spruce tree a great burly troll came up to him and said, "If you come chopping in my forest I shall kill you!"

When the lad heard this, he threw down his axe and scuttled home as fast as he could. He arrived terrified and breathless and told them what had happened. But his father called him a coward; the trolls had never scared him from chopping

---

* Trolls feature prominently in the folklore of Scandinavia especially in Norway. They were mythical creatures, usually giants, who lived in the mountains or in caves and were generally unfriendly and even dangerous to human beings. They were portrayed as ugly and grotesque in appearance and rather dim-witted. It was thought that they were immediately turned to stone if exposed to the sunlight and some large boulders were believed to be trolls whose fate it had been to end in this way. Their disappearance in modern times is said to be the result of their fear of Christianity and their inability to tolerate the ringing of church bells.

wood when he was young.

On the day after this the second son set off to the wood but he fared just the same. He had scarcely begun to chop at the spruce tree when the troll came up to him and said, "If you come chopping in my forest I shall kill you!"

The boy hardly dared to look at the troll. He threw down his axe and took to his heels as fast as his brother and probably even faster. When he came home his father was angry and said that the trolls had never scared him when he was young. On the third day Espen Ash Lad wanted to set off to the wood.

"Oh yes! You?" said the two older brothers. "Sure, you'll certainly manage it, you who have never set foot outside the door!"

Ash Lad didn't make any answer to this. He just asked if he could have a good pack of food. His mother did not have any meat so she hung the cooking pot over the fire to heat a little milk to make some cheese. This he put into his knapsack and went on his way.

When he had been chopping for a little while the troll came up to him and said, "If you come chopping in my forest I shall kill you!"

But Espen Ash Lad was not slow off the mark. He ran over to where his knapsack lay among the trees, fetched out the cheese and squeezed it so that the whey spurted out. "If you don't hold your tongue," he shouted at the troll, "I'll squeeze you just as I'm squeezing the water out of this white stone!"

"No! No! dear friend!" said the troll, "Please spare me and I will help you chop the wood."

Well, on that condition, Ash Lad said he was willing to spare the troll.

The troll was clever at chopping wood so they felled and cut up many cubic metres of timber during the day. Towards evening the troll said, "Now you must come home with me.

The Troll can't eat any more by Erik Werenskiold.
Illustration © O. Væring Eftf. AS.

My house is nearer than yours."

So Ash Lad went along and when they reached the troll's house the troll lit a fire in the fireplace while the boy went to fetch water for the porridge pot, but the two iron buckets were so big and heavy that he couldn't even lift them.

"Pooh!" he said to the troll, "It's hardly worth taking those two thimbles. I'll just go and fetch the whole well."

"No! No! my dear friend," said the troll, "I can't lose my well. You look after the fire; I'll go for the water." When he came back with the water they boiled up a huge pot of porridge.*

Espen Ash Lad then said "Let's have an eating contest. It's fine by me if it's all the same to you."

"Oh yes, sure!" replied the troll, for he felt he could easily hold his own at that game.

So they sat down at the table but Ash Lad secretly put his knapsack in front of him so he was able to spoon more porridge into the knapsack than he ate himself. When the knapsack was full he took his knife and made a slit in it. The troll looked at him but said nothing.

When they had eaten a good while longer the troll put down his spoon and said "No! I just can't eat any more."

"But you must eat," said Ash Lad. "I'm only half full yet. You should do what I did and cut a hole in your stomach, then you can eat as much as you wish."

---

* Porridge was the staple food throughout northern Europe for well over a thousand years. The traditional ritual of preparing it was to boil a cupful of water or milk, add a cupful of oatmeal and a little salt with the left hand and stir in a clockwise direction with the right hand until the preferred consistency was achieved. A bowl of cream or buttermilk was set on the table into which each spoonful was dipped. Bilberries or other wild berries were often added in season.

"But wouldn't that be very painful?" asked the troll.

"Oh, nothing to speak of," replied Ash Lad.

So the troll did as the boy said, and, as you must all know, that was the end of him.

Ash Lad then helped himself to all the silver and gold he found in the troll's mountain home and went home with it. He was able to pay off some of his father's debts.

The Doll in the Grass

Once upon a time there was a king who had twelve sons. When they were grown up he told them that they should go out into the world and find themselves a wife, but she should be able to spin and weave and sew a shirt in just one day, otherwise he would not accept her as a daughter-in-law. To each of them he gave a horse and a suit of armour, and so they set off into the world in order to find themselves wives. But they had travelled only a short distance when they said that they would not have Espen Ash Lad with them because he was no good for anything.

So Ash Lad had to be left behind – there was no doubt about that – and he didn't know what he would do or where he would go. He felt so upset that he got off his horse and sat down on the grass to weep. But after he had sat for a little while, one of the tufts of grass began to move about and out of it stepped a little white thing, and when it came closer Ash Lad saw that it was a lovely little girl but she was so very tiny. She went over to him and asked him if he would like to come down to see Doll in the Grass.

When he arrived down below, there was Doll in the Grass sitting on a chair: she was so beautiful and elegantly dressed, and she asked Ash Lad where he was going and what was the reason for his journey.

He told her that he was one of twelve brothers and that the king had given each of them a horse and a suit of armour and said that they had to go out into the world and find themselves a wife but she had to be able to spin and weave and sew a shirt in just one day. "If you can do that and if you will be my wife," Espen Ash Lad said to Doll in the Grass, "then I shall not travel any further." Yes, she would gladly do that and she hurried to spin, weave and sew a shirt; but it was so tiny, so very tiny, no longer than this _____

Ash Lad set off home with this shirt, but when he came to show it he was so ashamed because it was so tiny. Even so, the king said he should still have her and so Ash Lad set off again, happy and full of joy, to fetch his little sweetheart. When he came to Doll in the Grass he wanted to lift her up to sit in front of him on his horse, but no, she wouldn't agree to that – she said she would sit and ride in a silver spoon and she had two little white horses to pull her. So off they went, he on his horse and she in her silver spoon; the horses that pulled her were two little white mice.

All the time Ash Lad rode on the opposite side of the road as he was afraid that he might ride over her, for she was so very small. After they had gone some way along the road they came to a large lake where Ash Lad's horse took fright and shied over to the other side of the road overturning the spoon, and Doll in the Grass fell into the lake. Ash Lad was so distressed by this because he had no idea how he was going to get her out again. But soon up popped a merman holding her, and now she was as tall as any other grown up human being and even more beautiful than she had been before. So he set her in front of him on his horse and rode home.

When Espen arrived home all his brothers had arrived too, each one with his sweetheart, but they were all so ugly and horrid and so badly behaved that they had quarrelled and pulled each other's hair on the way home; and on their heads they wore hats which were daubed with tar and soot which had run down off the hats on to their faces so that they looked

She was so very tiny, by Theodor Kittelsen.
Illustration © O. Væring Eftf. AS.

uglier and more horrid than they were before.

When his brothers saw Ash Lad's sweetheart they were all very jealous of him; but the king was so delighted with them both that he chased all the others away. And so Ash Lad was wedded to Doll in the Grass and they lived a good and happy life together for a long, long time; and if they are not yet dead, then they are still alive.

Ash Lad and the Seven Foals

Once upon a time there was a poor couple who lived in a wretched hut deep inside the forest and they survived from hand to mouth, and only then with great difficulty; they had three sons and the youngest of them was called Espen Ash Lad for he did nothing but lounge and poke about among the ashes.

One day the eldest lad said that he would go out and earn his living. He was quickly given permission to do this and so he set out into the world. He walked on and on for the whole day until towards evening he came to a king's manor-house. The king stood on the steps and asked him where he was going.

"Oh, I'm just wandering about looking for employment, sir," said the lad.

"Will you work for me and keep an eye on my seven foals?" asked the king. "If you can guard them for a whole day, and in the evening tell me what they eat and drink, then you shall have the princess and half the kingdom. But if you can't, I shall cut three red stripes from your back. The lad thought that was easy work. He reckoned he could do that well enough.

Next morning, as dawn was breaking, the Master of the Horse let out the seven foals; and they ran off, with the lad after them, and away they went over hill and dale and through shrubberies and thickets. When he had chased round for some time he began to feel weary and, after he had held out for a while longer, he had had more than enough of all this watching.

Then he came to a cleft in the rock where an old woman sat spinning with her distaff; when she saw the lad chasing after the foals until the sweat ran down his face, she called out: "Come here, come here, my handsome son, and let me comb your hair."

The lad was willing enough and he sat down by the old woman and laid his head on her lap; and she combed his hair all day while he just lay and idled the time away.

Towards evening the lad was ready to go and said, "I might as well go straight home now, for it's no use going back to the manor."

"Wait until it's dark," said the old woman, "then the king's foals will return by this place and you can run home with them. Nobody will know that you have lain here all day instead of watching over the foals."

Then when the foals came she gave the lad a pitcher of water and a clump of moss to show the king and say that this was what the seven foals ate and drank.

In the evening when the lad came to see the king he asked, "Well now, have you kept watch carefully and faithfully all day long?"

"Yes, indeed I have," the lad replied.

"Then are you able to tell me what it is that my seven foals eat and drink?" the king asked.

So the lad produced the pitcher of water and the clump of moss that he had from the old woman, saying, "Here you see what they eat and here you see what they drink."

Then the king understood well enough just how he had kept watch and he fell into a rage and immediately ordered his men to chase him away but first they should cut three red stripes from his back and rub salt in them.

The foals released from the stable, by Alf Rolsen.
Illustration © O. Væring Eftf. AS.

When the lad reached home again you can imagine what sort of mood he was in. He had gone out to find work once, he said, but he would never do it again.

The next day the second son said that he wished to go out into the world and try his luck. His parents said "No!" and told him to look at his brother's back. But the lad would not give in; he stood by his wish and after a long, long time, he was given permission and went on his way.

When he had walked all day he, too, arrived at the king's manor-house and there stood the king out on the steps and asked where he was going; and when the lad replied that he was going about looking for work, the king said he could have a place with him, keeping an eye on his seven foals. Then the king set out the same punishment and the same reward for him as for his brother. Yes, the lad was willing to accept that so he took up the offer at once, for he thought he could look after the foals easily enough and tell the king what it was they ate and drank.

In the grey light of dawn the Master of Horse let out the seven foals and off they went over hill and dale – and the lad after them. But it all went the same as it had with his brother. When he had chased after the foals for a long, long time, until he was sweaty and tired, he passed by a cleft in the rock where an old woman sat spinning with her distaff and she called out to him, "Come here, come here, my handsome son, and let me comb your hair."

The lad thought this was a good idea, so he let the foals run wherever they liked and sat down with the old woman. So there he lay with his head on her lap, taking his ease the whole day.

When the foals came back in the evening, he too got a clump of moss and a pitcher of water from the old woman to show to the king.

When the king asked the second brother, "Can you tell me what it is my foals eat and drink?" the lad produced the clump of moss and the water pitcher saying, "Yes, here you see what they eat and here you see what they drink."

The king became very angry and ordered three red stripes to be cut from his back, salt rubbed into them and then he should be chased away back to his home at once. When the lad arrived home again he, too, told of all that had happened to him, and he, too, said that he had gone out looking for work once but he would never do it again.

On the third day Ash Lad wanted to set out. He said he wished to try to keep an eye on the seven foals himself. The other two brothers laughed at him and mocked him, saying, "When it all went so badly for us, what makes you think you will succeed? You hardly look as if you would stand a chance – you who have never done anything except lie there and poke among the ashes!"

"I will go, even so," said Ash Lad, "I've got it into my head, so I'll go."

However much his brothers laughed and his parents begged him not to go, it made no difference. Ash Lad went on his way.

When he had walked all day, he too arrived at the king's manor-house as darkness fell, and there stood the king out on the steps and asked him where he was going.

"I am wandering about looking for work," said Ash Lad.

"Where have you come from then?" the king asked. By now he wanted to be a little better informed before he took anyone into his service.

Ash Lad told the king where he came from and that he was the brother of the two others who had kept watch on the king's seven foals. Then he asked if now he could try to watch over them on the next day.

"Oh, Pshaw!" the king exclaimed – for he lost his temper

Ash Lad sets off by himself, by Erik Werenskiold.
Illustration © O. Væring Eftf. AS.

just hearing about them. "If you are the brother of those two you're not likely to be good for very much either. I've had enough of such fellows."

"Well, yes," replied Ash Lad, "but since I have come here, may I have permission just to try anyway?"

"Ah, well," said the king, "if you are determined to have your back flayed, it's all the same to me."

"For myself, I would much rather have the princess," said Espen Ash Lad.

Next morning in the grey light of dawn the Master of Horse let out the seven foals again, and off they went over hill and dale, through shrubberies and thickets – and Ash Lad after them.

When he had chased about for quite a long time, he too came to the cleft in the rock, and there the old woman sat spinning at her distaff and she called out, "Come here, come here, my handsome son, and let me comb your hair."

"Kiss my backside, kiss my backside!" Ash Lad shouted as he skipped and jumped and held on to the tail of one of the foals.

When he had got well past the cleft in the rock, the youngest foal said, "Get up on to my back for we have a long way to go yet." So this was what Ash Lad did and on they went, a long, long way.

"Can you see anything now?" asked the foal.

"No," said Ash Lad.

So, on they went a good distance further.

"Do you see anything now?" asked the foal.

"No, not yet," Ash Lad said.

When they had travelled much, much further, the foal again asked, "Do you see anything now, then?"

"Yes," said Ash Lad, "now I can see something white. It looks like the trunk of a big birch tree."

"Yes, that's it," said the foal, "we shall go in there."

When they reached the tree trunk, the eldest foal pushed it to one side and there, where the trunk had stood, was a door and inside it was a little room where there was little more than a fireplace and two bench seats; but behind the door hung a great rusty sword and a small pitcher.

"Are you able to wield that sword?" the foal asked.

Ash Lad tried but he couldn't manage it, so he had to take a drink from the pitcher – first one, then another, and still another, and then he could wield the sword easily.

"Good," said the foal. "Now you must take the sword with you, and on your wedding day you must cut off the heads of all seven of us, and then we shall become princes again – as we were before. For we are brothers of the princess whom you will have when you can tell the king what we eat and drink. There is a wicked troll who has cast a spell over us. When you have cut off our heads you must take great care to place each head at the tail of the body it belonged to before, and then the troll's spell will have no more power over us.

Ash Lad promised to do this and then they went further on.

When they had travelled a long, long way, the foal said, "Do you see anything?"

"No," said Ash Lad

So they went on a great distance further.

"And now?" the foal asked. "Do you see anything now?"

"No, nothing at all," said Ash Lad.

So they travelled on again over hill and dale for many, many miles.

"Now, then," the foal asked, "do you see anything now?"

"Yes, yes," said Ash Lad, "now I can see something like a blue streak far, far away."

"That is a river," said the foal, "and we have to cross it."

A long, fine bridge went over the river and when they

reached the other side they travelled on for a long, long way and then the foal again asked Ash Lad if he could see anything. Yes, this time he saw something, far, far away, that appeared to be black – it looked like a church tower.

"That's right," said the foal, "we shall go in there."

When the foals went into the churchyard they became men again and looked like princes, wearing such fine clothes that they shone brightly. They entered the church and there they received bread and wine from the priest standing before the altar. Ash Lad went in too. When the priest had laid hands on the princes and given them a Blessing, they went out to the churchyard again.

Ash Lad went out too but he took with him a flask of wine and some of the consecrated bread.

As soon as the seven princes came out of the church they were turned back into foals again. Ash Lad seated himself on the back of the youngest foal and they returned the same way they had come, but much, much faster.

First they crossed over the bridge, then past the trunk of the birch tree, and then past the old woman sitting in the cleft of the rock spinning at her distaff. They went by so fast that Ash Lad didn't hear what the old woman screamed at him, but he heard enough to understand that she was very angry.

It was almost dark when they got back to the king's manor-house in the evening. The king himself stood in the courtyard waiting for them.

"Have you watched carefully and faithfully the whole day?" the king asked Ash Lad.

"I've done my best," Espen replied.

"Then you can tell me what my seven foals eat and drink?" the king asked.

Ash Lad then took out the consecrated bread and the flask of wine and showed them to the king.

"Here you see what they eat and here you see what they drink," he said.

"Yes, you have watched carefully and faithfully," the king said, "and you shall have the princess and half the kingdom."

So all was made ready for the wedding and the king said it should be so magnificent and so grand that everyone would hear of it and want to know about it.

But just as they were sitting down to the wedding feast, the bridegroom stood up and went down to the stables. He said he had forgotten something there which he must go and attend to. When he got there he did what the foals had told him he must do and cut off the heads of all seven of them: first the eldest, then all the rest according to their age. Then he carefully placed each head at the tail of the foal it belonged to, and as he did this they all became princes again.

When Ash Lad returned to the wedding feast accompanied by the seven princes, the king was so overjoyed that he not only kissed him but embaced him too, while his bride was even more delighted with him than she had been before.

"Half the kingdom is yours already," said the king, "and the other half shall be yours after my death; for my sons can easily get lands and kingdoms for themselves now that they are princes again.

So it is very likely that there was much joy and merriment at that wedding.

I was there too but no-one had any time to give a thought to me, so I got nothing more than a slice of cake with butter on, and that I put down on the stove so the butter ran, the cake was burnt, and I didn't get even the slightest crumb.

The Troll who had no heart in his body

There was once a king who had seven sons and he loved them all so much that he never wanted to be without them all at the same time: one must always be with him. Now, when they were grown up six of them wanted to go out into the world to seek a wife but their father kept the youngest one at home and the others were to bring a princess back to the palace for him.

The king gave the six the finest clothes anyone had ever seen, so splendid that the light shone from them from far away, and each one had a horse which cost many, many hundreds of gold coins. And so they set off. When they had visited many palaces and seen many princesses they came at last to a king who had six daughters; such beautiful princesses they had never before set eyes on and so they began to woo them, each one his own princess, and when they had made them their sweethearts they set off home again; but they were so much in love with their own sweethearts that they completely forgot that they were supposed to bring back with them a princess for their youngest brother Espen Ash Lad who had stayed at home.

When they had travelled quite some distance on the way home they came right beside a steep mountain, just like a wall. Here a troll lived. He came out and saw them and he fixed his eyes on them and turned them all to stone, princes and princesses alike.

The king waited and waited for his six sons but however

49

long he waited none of them came. He went about in great sorrow and became so sad that he said he could never be really happy again. "If I did not have you left with me," he said to Ash Lad, "I would not wish to live any longer; I feel so sad at the loss of your brothers."

"Well now," said Ash Lad, "I've been thinking of asking you to let me go and find them."

"No, I'll not let you do that," said his father, "for then you will also be lost to me."

But Ash Lad was determined to go. He begged and he prayed until in the end the king had to let him go. Now the king had no other horse to give him except an old broken-winded nag, for the six other sons and their retinue had taken all his best horses. But Ash Lad didn't worry himself about that; he just mounted himself on to the old, mangy horse and said, "Goodbye, father, I'll be sure to come back, and perhaps I'll have my brothers with me."

And with that he set off.

When he had ridden a while he came across a raven lying on the road flapping its wings and with no strength to move because it was so hungry.

"Oh! Dear friend," said the raven, "Give me a little food and then I'll help you when you are in real need."

"I don't have much food," said the prince, "and you don't look as if you will be able to help me much either. But even so I can spare you a little for I can see that you really need it."

So he gave the raven a little of the food he had brought with him.

Now when he had travelled a little further he came to a stream and there he found a great salmon which had become stranded on dry land. It was leaping and thrashing around and was unable to get itself back into the water again.

"Oh! Dear friend," the salmon said to the prince. "Help me

get back into the water and I promise I'll help you when you are in real need."

"Any help you can give me won't amount to much I expect," the prince replied, "but it would be a pity to let you lie there and starve to death."

So he heaved the fish back into the stream again.

He travelled on a long, long way and then he met a wolf which was so hungry that it lay on the road and had to drag itself along.

"Dear friend!" said the wolf. "Let me have your horse. I'm so hungry that the wind is whistling through my guts. I haven't had a proper meal for two years."

"No," said Ash Lad, "I can't let you have my horse; first I come across a raven and I have to give it my food; then I find a salmon and I have to help it back into the water; and now you want my horse. That can't be done, for then I'll have nothing to ride on.

"But, dear friend," said Greylegs, the wolf, "you have to help me. You can ride on my back," he said, "and then I will help you when you are in real need."

"Well, any help I get from you probably won't amount to much," said the prince, "but since you are so dreadfully hungry you can have the horse."

So, when the wolf had eaten up the horse, Ash Lad fixed the bit to the wolf's jaws and put the saddle on its back, and the wolf was now so strong after all that it had eaten that it set off with the prince faster than he had ever ridden before.

"Now, when we have ridden a little further," said Greylegs, "I'll show you where the troll lives." And a little later on they came to it.

"Look, here is the troll's house," said the wolf to Ash Lad, "and there you can see your six brothers and their six brides whom the troll has turned to stone. Over there is the door to

51

the troll's house and through that you have to go."

"No, I daren't do that," said the prince. "The troll will kill me."

"Oh no, he won't," replied the wolf. "When you go in there you will meet a princess who will tell you what you have to do to get rid of the troll. But you must do exactly what she tells you."

Well, Ash Lad then went in, but he was certainly afraid. When he came inside, the troll was not there, but in one of the rooms sat the princess, just as the wolf had said. Espen Ash Lad had never before seen such a beautiful princess.

"Oh, Heaven help you! How did you get here?" said the princess. "It will surely be the death of you. Nobody can kill the troll who lives here because he has no heart in his body."

"Well, now that I am here," said Ash Lad, "I might as well try. I'll try to rescue both you and my brothers who are standing out there turned to stone."

"Since you insist on staying then, we must work out a plan," said the princess. "You must creep under the bed over there and you must listen carefully to what I say to the troll. But, above all, you must lie absolutely quiet."

He crept under the bed and he had scarcely got under before the troll came in.

"Ha!" said the troll, "there's the smell of a Christian man in here!"

"Yes," said the princess, "a magpie came flying with a man's bone in its beak and dropped it down the chimney. Of course I hurried to get rid of it but the smell obviously doesn't go away quickly."

So the troll said nothing more about it. When evening came they went to bed.

When they had been lying there for a while, the princess said, "There is something I would like to ask you about, if

Espen Ash Lad and the wolf, by Theodor Kittelsen.
Illustration © O. Væring Eftf. AS.

only I dared."

"And what is that?" asked the troll.

"It is, where do you keep your heart since you don't keep it in your body?" asked the princess.

"Ah, that's something you have no business to concern yourself with, but, if you must know, it lies under the doorsill."

"Aha!" said Ash Lad to himself under the bed. "We'll have a look there and see if we can find it."

The next morning the troll was up very early and went off into the woods. He was hardly out of the house before Ash Lad and the princess began to search under the doorsill for his heart. But however much they dug and searched there was nothing to be found.

"He has tricked us this time," said the princess, "but we'll try again."

So she gathered all the prettiest flowers she could find and scattered them round the doorsill which they had replaced exactly as it was before. When it was time for the troll to come home again Ash Lad crept under the bed. No sooner was he safely underneath than the troll appeared.

"Faugh!" he exclaimed, "there's the smell of a Christian man in here!"

"Yes," said the princess, "a magpie came flying with a man's bone in its beak and dropped it down the chimney again. I hurried as much as I could to get it out but that's probably what you can smell."

The troll said nothing more about it. A little later he asked who it was who had scattered flowers round the doorsill.

"Oh, I did, of course," said the princess.

"And what was the point of doing that?" asked the troll.

"Oh, I'm so fond of you that I had to do it when I knew that your heart is lying there," said the princess.

"Really?" said the troll, "but, you know, it isn't lying there at all."

When they had gone to bed that evening the princess asked again where the troll kept his heart, for, she said, she was so fond of him that she really would like to know.

"Ah well," said the troll, "it is lying in that cupboard over there by the wall."

"Aha!" thought both Ash Lad and the princess, "then we shall try and find it there."

The next morning the troll was away early and went off to the woods again. And just as soon as he had gone Ash Lad and the princess were in the cupboard searching for his heart but however much they searched they could find nothing there either.

"Ah well!" said the princess, "we'll try him again."

So she decked out the cupboard with flowers and garlands, and when evening came Ash Lad crept under the bed again. Then in came the troll.

"Faugh!" he said, "there's the smell of a Christian man in here."

"Yes," said the princess. "A little time ago a magpie came flying with a man's bone in its beak and dropped it down the chimney. I hurried as fast as I could to get it out again but that is probably what the smell is."

When the troll heard that he said no more about it; but when he saw that flowers and garlands were hanging round the cupboard he asked who it was who had done that, and of course, it was the princess.

"And what's the point of all that nonsense?" asked the troll.

"Oh," said the princess, "I'm so very fond of you that I just had to do it when I knew that your heart was lying there."

"How can you be so silly as to believe that?"

"Of course I had to believe it when that was what you told

me," said the princess.

"Oh, you are a funny one," said the troll. "You will never find the place where my heart is."

"But I would like to know so very much just where it is," said the princess.

So the troll couldn't resist any longer and he had to give in and he said, "Far, far away there is a lake and in that lake there is an island; and on that island there stands a church; and in that church there is a well; and in that well a duck is swimming; and in that duck there is an egg; and inside that egg is where my heart is; you dear sweetheart."

Early the next morning – it was before dawn – the troll hurried off to the woods again.

"Now I must be going too," said Espen Ash Lad, "if only I knew how to find the way."

He said a long goodbye to the princess, and then when he came out of the troll's house there stood the wolf patiently waiting. Ash Lad told the wolf all that had happened in the troll's house and said that now he wanted to go to the well in the church, if only he knew the way.

"Just sit yourself up on my back," said the wolf, "and I'm sure I can find the way for you."

So off they went so fast that the wind whistled round them, over moorland and mountains, over hills and dales. When they had travelled for many, many days, at last they came to the lake. The prince had no idea how to get across it, but the wolf said he was not to worry about that, and it just set off across the water with the prince on its back and swam over to the island. Here they found the church, but the church keys were hanging high, high up on top of the tower, and at first the prince had no idea how he would get them down.

"You must call for the raven," said the wolf.

The prince did that and almost immediately the raven

appeared and flew up to get the keys and so the prince was able to get into the church. Then when he came to the well there was the duck swimming to and fro just as the troll had said. He stood there and coaxed it and coaxed it until at last he managed to coax it over to him and he was able to get hold of it, but just as he was lifting it out of the water it dropped the egg down into the well and Ash Lad had no idea how he was going to get it out again.

"Now you must call for the salmon," said the wolf, and so the prince did that and the salmon came and brought up the egg. The wolf then told Ash Lad to squeeze it and, as soon as he did, the troll screamed.

"Squeeze it again," said the wolf, and when Ash Lad did that the troll screamed even more pitifully and begged so plaintively and so graciously for mercy, saying he would do anything the prince wished if only he would not squeeze his heart again.

The wolf said, "Tell him that if he will bring back to life your six brothers and their brides whom he has turned to stone, then you will spare his life."

Ash Lad did this and the troll said, "Yes," he would do that straight away, so the six brothers were restored to life as princes and their brides as princesses.

"Now you can crush the egg to pieces," said the wolf.

So Ash Lad squeezed the egg so that it was crushed and with that the troll burst.

That was the end of the troll; and Ash Lad rode on the wolf's back to the troll's house and there stood all his six brothers alive and happy with their brides. Ash Lad went into the troll's house in the mountain to find his own bride and they all went home together to the king's manor.

The old king was so delighted when all his seven sons came home again, each one with his own bride.

"The most beautiful of all the princesses is Espen Ash Lad's bride," said the king, "and he shall sit with her at the head of the table."

So they held a great wedding feast and celebrated long and merrily. And if they have not yet come to the end of their celebrations, well then they are still going on...

He who is beloved by women will never be in need

Once upon a time there were three brothers: I don't quite know how it had come about but each of them had been given the right to have one wish, whatever they chose. Two of them didn't spend much time thinking about this: they wished that every time they put their hands in their pockets they would always find some money there; for, they said, "when a man has as much money as he would like, he will always be able to get on in the world." But the youngest brother preferred to wish for something better; he chose to wish that every woman would fall in love with him as soon she set eyes on him: and that, as you will soon hear, was far better than money and possessions.

When they had all made their wishes, the two older brothers were ready to set out into the world and the youngest brother, Espen Ash Lad, asked if he could come along with them but they wouldn't agree to that on any account.

"Wherever we go," they said, "we shall be treated as earls and princes, but you, you miserable wretch who have nothing and will never have anything, do you think anyone will take any notice of you?"

"Even so," said Ash Lad, "I'd still like to come with you. It's possible that a bit of roast meat may happen to fall my way when I am in the company of such great men."

At long last he was allowed to go with them but only if he

would be their servant; otherwise they would have nothing to do with him.

When they had travelled for a day or so they came to an inn where the two who had money decided to stay and called for meat and fish, brandy and mead, and everything that was good, but Ash Lad had to look after all the luggage that belonged to the two important men. As he went to and fro and wandered about in the inn-yard the innkeeper's wife came to look out of the window and she caught sight of the servant of the two important guests, and she thought she had never before seen such a good-looking man; she stared and stared at him and the longer she stared the more handsome she thought he was.

"What, by the Devil's skin and bones, is it you are gaping and staring at through the window?" said her husband. "It would be better if you saw to the cooking of the roast pig than standing there idly hanging about; you must know what important guests we have in the house today."

"Oh, I don't trouble myself with such trash," said the old woman. "If they don't like it here they can go back to where they came from. But just come over here and look at that lad out there in the yard! I have never in all my life seen such a handsome fellow. If you agree, let us ask him in and give him a little treat. He probably hasn't got much to get through life with, poor lad."

"Have you lost the little sense you ever had, woman?" said her husband. "Get into the kitchen with you and tend to the fire, don't stand there gaping at strange men."

There was nothing his wife could do except go out into the kitchen and attend to the cooking. She wasn't allowed to ask the lad in and give him even a little treat, but just when she was standing in the kitchen ready to spit the roast pig, she gave herself an excuse to run out into the inn-yard to give Ash Lad a pair of scissors which, just if he clipped them in the air, would cut out the finest clothes ever seen, of silk and velvet and of everything that was of the best. "This you shall have because you are so handsome," said the innkeeper's wife.

Now when the two brothers had had their fill of good food, both roast and boiled, they were ready to set off again, and Ash Lad had to stand at the back of their coach and be their servant. So they travelled again quite a long way until they came to another inn where the brothers went inside, except Espen Ash Lad who had no money. They would not allow him in with them – he had to remain outside and look after all their luggage, and they told him, "If anyone asks whose servant you are, say that we are two foreign princes."

Now things happened exactly as they had before; while Ash Lad was standing out in the inn-yard just hanging about, the innkeeper's wife came over to the window and caught sight of him and she fell for him just like the first innkeeper's wife. She stood and stared, and stared, and couldn't have enough of him. Then her husband came dashing into the room with something the princes had ordered.

"Don't stand there staring like a cow at a barn door," said the man, "just get into the kitchen, woman, and attend to the fish-kettle. You know what important guests we have in the house today, don't you?"

"I don't trouble myself with such trash, not I!" said his wife. "If they don't like what they get then they can have what they brought with them. But just come here and you'll see what I can see. Never in all my life have I seen such a handsome man as the one out there in the yard. If you agree with me, we will ask him in and give him a little treat. He looks as if he needs it, poor lad! Oh, isn't he just so wonderfully handsome!"

"You never did have much sense," said her husband, "and

I can see that you have completely lost the little you did have."

He was even more angry than the other innkeeper and drove his wife out into the kitchen. "Get out into the kitchen with you," he said, "and don't just stand gaping at young lads."

So she had to go out to the kitchen and look after the fish-kettle, and she dare not give Ash Lad a treat for she was afraid of her husband. But as she stood making up the fire she made an excuse to go out to the yard and she gave Ash Lad a table cloth which, if he just spread it out, would serve up the finest dishes it was possible to imagine.

"This you shall have because you are so handsome," she said to Ash Lad.

Now when the two brothers had eaten and drunk of all that was to be found in the inn and had paid their costly bill, they set off again, with Espen Ash Lad standing at the back of their coach. When they had travelled until they were hungry they went into an inn and called for all they could think of which was the best and most expensive.

"For," they said, "we are two kings on our travels and we have as much money as if it grew like grass." When the innkeeper heard this there was such a roasting and broiling that the smell wafted as far away as the nearest neighbour's house. The innkeeper didn't know how he was going to find everything for the two kings, but Ash Lad had to stand outside again and keep an eye on the luggage in the coach.

Then everything happened just as it had on the two previous occasions: the innkeeper's wife came to peep out of the window and she saw the servant standing by the coach and she had never set eyes on such a handsome lad before. She looked and she looked, and the more she gazed at him the more handsome he seemed to be. The innkeeper came dashing through the room with some food the two travelling kings had ordered, and he was not at all pleased when he saw his wife standing gaping out of the window.

He said, "Don't you know any better than to stand staring out of the window when we have such important guests in the house? Get into the kitchen at once and attend to the cream porridge."

"Oh, there's no great hurry as far as I'm concerned," his wife replied. "If they can't wait until the porridge is ready they can go off without it. Now just come and look here! I have never before seen such a handsome lad as the one standing out there in the yard. If you agree with me, let us ask him inside and give him a little treat, for he certainly looks as if he could do with it. Oh, he's so handsome it touches my heart!"

"You've been a flirt all your life, and you still are," her husband said – he was so angry that he could barely stand still.

"But if you don't come and look after the porridge I'll put my foot behind you, you see if I don't."

At that his wife had to hurry off to the kitchen as fast as she could, for she knew her husband was not one to be trifled with; but even so she slipped out into the yard and gave Ash Lad a tap. "When you turn on this tap," she said, "you will get the finest drinks you can wish for, mead, wine and brandy. This you shall have because you are so very handsome."

When the two brothers had eaten and drunk all they wanted they travelled on from the inn with Ash Lad again standing at the back of the coach as their servant. They then drove for a great distance until they came to a king's palace where the two older brothers announced themselves as sons of an emperor. They were very well treated and looked after as they had plenty of money and were so finely dressed that they stood out brightly from a long way off. They were given rooms in the palace and the king did all he could to make a fuss of them.

But Ash Lad still wore the same tattered clothes he was wearing when he left home. He didn't have a penny in his pocket, so he was taken away by the palace guards and rowed across to an island where they put all the beggars and rogues who came to the palace. The king had ordered this so that they would not disturb the gaiety at the palace when they appeared looking so ragged and scruffy. Only enough food was sent out there every day to keep body and soul together. Espen's brothers actually saw the guards row him out to the island but they were only too glad to be rid of him and showed not the slightest concern for him.

When Ash Lad arrived on the island he just took out his pair of scissors and clipped in the air with them and the scissors made the finest clothes of velvet and silk that anyone could wish for, so that the beggars out on the island were dressed more grandly than the king and everyone else who was at the palace. Then Ash Lad took out his tablecloth and spread it out and so the beggars were also well provided with food. No banquet at the king's palace had ever served such a feast as was seen on that day on the beggars' island.

"I expect you are all thirsty too," said Ash Lad, and he took out his tap and gave it a little turn, and so the beggars all had something to drink: ale and mead which tasted better than anything even the king himself had tasted in his entire life.

When those who were to bring food to the island for the scruffy beggars came rowing over with their cold porridge scrapings and cheese rinds – for that was the food they were to have – the beggars on the island wouldn't even taste them. The king's men were very surprised by this but they were even more astonished when they had a good look at the beggars and saw how grandly clothed they were.

They thought they must be a gathering of emperors or popes and that they had rowed out to the wrong island, but when they looked round more closely they recognised just where they were. So they came to the conclusion that it must be the one they had rowed out the day before who had brought the beggars on the island all this finery.

When they returned to the palace they were not slow to tell that the man they had rowed out the day before had clothed all the beggars so magnificently that riches seemed to drip from them.

"As for the porridge and cheese we took for them," they said, "they wouldn't even taste them, so haughty have they become." One of the king's men had discovered that the lad had a pair of scissors which he had used to cut out the clothes: "when he holds the scissors up in the air," he said, "and snips with them, he cuts out nothing but silk and velvet."

When the princess heard this she didn't have a moment's peace until she got to see this lad and his scissors that cut only silk and velvet out of the air. Such a pair of scissors was surely worth having, she thought, for then she could have all the fine clothes she wished for. So she pleaded with the king so long that he had to send a messenger for the lad who owned the scissors, and when he came to the palace the princess asked him if it were true that he had such a pair of scissors and if he would sell them to her.

Yes, said Ash Lad, he did, indeed, have such a pair of scissors but he was certainly not willing to sell them. He then took the scissors from his pocket and snipped with them up in the air so that strips of silk and pieces of velvet flew all round her ears.

"Oh! You must sell me these scissors," said the princess, "you can ask whatever you like for them but I really must have them."

"No," he said, he would not sell them at any price for such a pair of scissors he would never have again. While they stood and haggled over the scissors, the princess had a better look at Espen Ash Lad and, just like the innkeepers' wives, she thought that she had never seen such a handsome fellow before.

She began to haggle over the scissors again and she begged and begged Ash Lad to sell them. He could ask as much gold as he liked, it was all the same to her just so long as she had the scissors.

"No," said Ash Lad, "I will not sell them, I will not. But, I have an idea. If I could be allowed to sleep one night on the floor, right by the door, in the princess's bedroom, then she shall have them. I shall do her no harm, but if she is afraid, she may, if she wishes, have two men to keep watch in the room."

Yes, the princess felt sure that could be arranged: if only she could have the scissors she would be content to agree to that. So that night Espen Ash Lad lay on the floor in the princess's room and two men kept watch. The princess didn't get much sleep. There were better things to do, for she just had to keep opening her eyes to peep at Ash Lad, and this went on the whole night. No sooner had she closed her eyes than she had to peep at him again, she thought he was so handsome.

The next morning Ash Lad was rowed out again to the beggars' island but when they came with the porridge scrapings and the cheese parings from the palace no-one would taste them that day either, and those who brought them were even more surprised than before. One of them had discovered that the lad who had the scissors also owned a table cloth and he had only to spread it out and he had all the best food he could wish for. When he came back to the palace he lost no time in telling all about it, "Such roasts and such creamy porridge had never been seen even in the king's palace," he said.

When the princess heard this she told the king about it and she begged and begged and in the end he had to send a messenger to the island to find the lad who owned the table cloth, and so Ash Lad came up to the palace again. The princess said she must have the table cloth from him and she offered gold and lush green woods for it but Ash Lad flatly refused to sell for anything or for any price.

"But," he said, "if I may be allowed to lie on the truckle-bed in the princess's bedroom tonight, then she shall have my table cloth. I shall, of course, do her no harm but if she is afraid, she may, if she wishes, have four men in the room to keep watch."

Yes, the princess would agree to that and Ash Lad lay on the truckle-bed beside the princess and four men stood on guard, but if the princess had had little sleep on the night before, she had even less that night. She had scarcely even closed her eyes, she just had to lie and look at that handsome lad the whole night, and even then she thought the night was too short.

The next morning Ash Lad was once again rowed out to the beggars' island but that was not what the princess wished, for she had become so utterly fond of him. There was nothing to be done about it though – he had to go out there again and that was the end of it. When those from the palace who came with the porridge and cheese crusts which were intended for the beggars' food, there was not a single one who would taste what the king had sent, and those from the palace were not at all surprised, but they still thought it strange that not one of them was thirsty.

But then one of the king's messengers discovered that the lad who had owned the scissors and the table cloth also had a tap which he only had to turn a little and he could obtain the finest drinks that anyone could imagine – ale and mead and wine. When he came back to the palace he couldn't hold his tongue any more this time than on the two previous occasions and he spread the news far and wide of this tap from which it was so easy to get all kinds of drinks.

"Such ale and mead have never been tasted in the king's

palace," he said, "they are sweeter than either honey or syrup."

When the princess heard this she couldn't wait to get her hands on this tap, and neither had she anything against coming to some agreement with the lad who owned it. So she went to the king again and asked him to send a messenger to the beggars' island for the lad who had owned the scissors and the table cloth, for now, she said, he had another thing that was well worth having, and when the king heard that this was a tap which would pour out the best ale and the best wine that anyone could wish to drink, just by a single turn on the tap, he didn't waste any time before he sent his messenger.

So when Ash Lad came up to the palace the princess asked him if it was true that he had such a tap.

"Yes," said Espen Ash Lad, he had it in his waistcoat pocket, but when the princess tried with all her might to buy it, Ash Lad replied, as he had on the previous occasions, that there was no way he was prepared to sell it, even if the princess offered him half the kingdom for it.

"But all the same," he added, "if I could be allowed to lie on the princess's bed, on top of the quilt, that night, then she could have his tap. I shall do her no harm but if she is afraid she may, if she wishes, have eight men in the room to keep watch."

"Oh, no!" said the princess, "that's not necessary." She knew him so well, now. And so Ash Lad lay that night beside the princess on her bed-quilt. But if she hadn't slept much on the two previous nights, she had even less sleep that night. She couldn't close her eyes the whole night for she just had to lie and look at Espen Ash Lad who lay beside her.

When she got up in the morning and they were going to row Ash Lad out to the beggars' island again, she asked them to wait a little while. She hurried in to see the king and asked him with heartfelt charm if she could have Espen Ash Lad for her husband, for she was so much in love with him that if she could not have him she had no wish to live.

"Well yes, of course you shall have him if that is what you really wish," said the king. "The one who owns such things is just as rich as you."

So Ash Lad won the princess and half the kingdom – the other half he would have when the king died – and so all was well. As for his brothers, who had always been so unkind to him, he sent them off to the beggars' island. "They can stay there," said Ash Lad, "until they have found out who is better off, the man who has his pockets full of money or the man whom all women fall in love with."

I can't imagine either that it would be of much help on beggars' island to put your hand in your pocket and jingle your money. And if Ash Lad hasn't taken them off the island they are still there, walking about eating cold porridge and cheese rinds every day.

Ash Lad made the Princess say 'That's a lie'

There was once a king who had a daughter who was such a terrible liar that there was no-one who was as dreadful as she was. So he let it be known that anyone who could tell such a story as would get the princess herself to say, "That's a lie", would have both her and half the kingdom. Many came to try, for everyone would have been very glad to have the princess and half the kingdom, but all of them failed badly.

However, there were three brothers who were keen to try their luck. The two eldest set out first but they did no better than all the others who had tried. So the youngest, Espen Ash Lad, set off and he met the princess in the cattle shed.

"Good day!" he said, "I'm pleased to meet you."

"Good day!" she replied, "I'm pleased to meet you too."

"I'm sure your cattle shed is not as big as ours," she then said, "for when two shepherds stand, one at each end, and blow on their ram's horns, they can't hear each other."

"Oh, yes it is," said Ash Lad. "Ours is much bigger, for when a cow has been with the bull at one end of the shed, she doesn't have her calf until she gets to the other end."

"Oh, is that so?" said the princess. "Well, you can't have as big an ox as we have. You can see it over there! When two men sit, one on each horn, they are unable to reach each other with a five metre pole."

"Pooh!" said Ash Lad. "We have an ox so big that when two men are sitting, one on each horn, blowing on a lur,* they

"You can't have as big an ox as ours," said the princess, by Erik Werenskiold. Illustration © O. Væring Eftf. AS.

A lur, photograph copyright Norsk Skogmuseum, Elverum.

*A lur is a wind instrument like a long horn – about 150cms – but it has no finger holes. The sound could carry for a great distance. There is no other word in English for the lur. It is often described as a birch trumpet chiefly because the two pieces of hollowed-out spruce wood of which it was made were bound together by strips of birch bark. It was known in Norway as the neverlur or birch-bark lur, and was popularly known as the shepherd's lur or milk-maid's lur since it was used to call the goats and cattle home from the forest to be milked and to be sheltered for the night. It was widely used in the Scandinavian countries from the early Middle Ages until modern times.

can't hear each other."

"Oh, indeed!" said the princess, "but you don't have as much milk as we do. For we milk our cows into great wooden tubs and carry it indoors and pour it into enormous vats and make it into huge cheeses."

"Oh, is that so?" said Ash Lad. "Well, we milk ours into great troughs, take them indoors in carts and pour the milk into huge brewing vats to make cheeses as big as a house. And we had a grey mare to tread the cheese and one day she had a foal in the cheese, and after we had been eating into the cheese for seven years we found a big grey horse in it.

One day I was driving this horse to the mill when its backbone broke; but I knew how to deal with that. I took a young spruce tree and put that into the horse's back instead of a backbone, and that horse had no other backbone as long as we had it. But the tree grew and became so tall that I climbed up to Heaven by it and when I got there I saw the Virgin Mary sitting weaving bristle rope out of a broth-soup.

All at once the spruce tree broke and so I couldn't get down again, but the Virgin Mary lowered me down on one of the ropes and I landed right into a fox's den, and there sat my mother and your father cobbling shoes. Suddenly my mother hit out at your father with such a blow that scabby skin and scurf flew off him in a shower."

"That's a lie!" said the princess. "My father never had scabby skin and scurf in all his life."

And so Ash Lad won both the princess and half the kingdom.

Peter, Paul and Espen Ash Lad

Once upon a time there was a man who had three sons named Peter, Paul and Espen Ash Lad, but except for his three sons he had very little else. He was so poor that he didn't even own the hook on the wall. So he told his sons over and over again that they would have to go out into the world and earn their bread, for at home with him there was nothing except starvation to look forward to.

Quite a long way from their house was the king's manor-house and just outside the king's windows an oak tree had grown so tall and broad that it cut out the light from the house. The king had offered a great deal of money to anyone who could cut down the oak tree but no-one had been able to do it because, as soon as a chip was cut off the tree, two others sprang up in its place.

The king also wished to have a well which would hold water the whole year round, for all his neighbours had such a well while he didn't have one, and he thought that was shameful. The king had offered both money and gifts to anyone who could dig him a well that would hold water all the year round, but no-one had been able to do it because the manor-house stood high, high up on a hill, and after they had dug down no more than a few inches they came to the hard bedrock. But the king had taken it into his head that he would have these tasks done, so he had it proclaimed in all the churches far and wide that the man who could cut down the big oak tree at the manor and dig him a well which would hold water the whole year

Oak tree outside the King's house, by Theodor Kittelsen.
Illustration © O. Væring Eftf. AS.

round would have the king's daughter and half the kingdom.

There were many who were keen to try their luck but all their hewing and chopping and all their digging and delving came to nothing. The oak tree became bigger and broader at every stroke of the axe, and the rock didn't get any softer either. After a while the three brothers also wanted to go and try their luck and their father was highly delighted with this, for even if they didn't win the king's daughter and half the kingdom, he thought it might happen that they would find employment with a good master – and he couldn't wish for anything more. So when the brothers decided that they wished to go to the king's manor their father agreed without any hesitation, and so Peter, Paul and Espen Ash Lad set off.

They had gone quite some way when they came to a spruce wood and right above it was a steep hillside where they heard something chopping and hewing.

"I'm just wondering what it is that's chopping up there on the hillside," said Espen.

"You always try to be so clever with your wonderings," said Peter and Paul. "What is there to wonder about if there's a woodcutter hewing away up on the hillside?"

"I'd just like to see what it is, all the same," said Espen. And with that off he went.

"Oh, you're such a child!" his brothers called after him. "Enjoy yourself learning how to walk as well."

But Espen took notice of them. He set off up the hill towards where he heard the chopping and when he reached the place he saw that it was just an axe chopping away all by itself at the trunk of a spruce tree.

"Good day," said Espen Ash Lad, "are you standing there chopping all by yourself?"

"Yes," the axe replied. "I've been standing here chopping for a very long time waiting for you."

"Well now," said Espen Askeladd, "here I am."

He took hold of the axe, pulled the axe head off the haft and stuffed both the axe and the haft into his knapsack. When he came down to his brothers again they laughed at him and mocked him.

"So, what strange thing was it you saw up on the hill then?" they asked.

"Oh, it was only an axe we heard," said Espen.

When they had gone a while longer they came under a crag and somewhere above they heard the sound of something digging using a pick and shovel.

"I'm just wondering what it is that's picking and digging up on that crag?" asked Espen Ash Lad.

"Oh, you're always so clever with your wonderings, aren't you?" Peter and Paul jeered again. "Have you never heard the birds pecking at the trees before?"

"Of course I have," Espen replied, "but I'd just like to see what it is, all the same."

However much they both laughed and made fun of him he took no notice but set off up the crag and when he came near the top he saw a spade picking and digging all by itself.

"Good day," he said. "Are you just standing there picking and digging all by yourself?"

"Yes, that is what I'm doing," said the spade, "And I have stood here picking and digging for a very long time waiting for you."

"Well now, here I am," said Espen.

He took hold of the spade, knocked off the handle and hid the spade in his knapsack. He then went down to his brothers again.

"No doubt it was something very unusual you saw up there on the crag?" laughed Peter and Paul together.

"Oh, it was nothing very much," said Espen, "it was only a

spade we heard."

So they then went on together again for quite a long way until they came to a stream. All three of them were now thirsty after they had travelled for so long, so they lay down beside the stream to have a drink.

"I'm just wondering where this water comes from," said Espen.

"If you weren't crazy before then you very soon will be, with everything you go wondering about. Now you wonder where the stream comes from? Have you never seen water rising up from a spring in the ground?"

"Yes," Espen replied, "but, all the same, I would very much like to see where it comes from."

So off he went along the stream and however much his brothers called after him and made fun of him, he took no notice. He just went on his way.

As he climbed up and up, the stream became smaller and smaller, and when he had gone some way further he found a walnut – and out of this the water trickled.

"Good day," said Espen Ash Lad, "so, you're just lying there trickling and running all by yourself?"

"Yes, that's what I'm doing," said the walnut. "I have been lying here trickling and running for a very long time waiting for you."

"Well now," said Espen, "Here I am."

He then took a clump of moss and plugged up the hole in the walnut so that the water could not run out and then put the walnut in his knapsack and set off again down to his brothers.

"Well now," his brothers taunted him, "have you discovered where the water comes from? It must have been a very unusual sight, that's for sure."

"Oh no," said Espen, "it was only a hole it ran out of." And the others laughed and made fun of him again, but Espen took no notice, just saying "Yes, but I enjoyed seeing it all the same."

When they had gone some way further on they came to the king's manor. Everybody in the kingdom had heard that they could win the princess and half the kingdom if they could cut down the great oak tree and dig a well for the king and so many had come to try their luck that the oak tree was now twice as tall and broad as it was at first, for, of course, two chips grew for each one that the axe cut off. So the king decided that, as a penalty, those who tried to fell the oak and failed should be put on an island and have both their ears cut off.

The two brothers didn't let themselves be put off by this: they were so sure that they could fell the oak tree. Peter, who was the oldest, tried his luck first; but it went with him as it had with all the others who had chopped at the oak tree; for every chip he cut from the tree two more grew in its place. So the king's men seized him, cut off both his ears and sent him out to the island.

Now it was Paul's turn to try, but it all went just the same for him; when he had chopped just two or three times everyone could see that the oak tree just grew bigger, so the king's men seized him too and sent him out to the island, cutting off his ears even closer for they thought he should have learned from the fate of his brother and taken better care of himself.

Then Espen wanted to try.

The king was annoyed with him after what had happened to his brothers and said, "If you really want to look like a sheep marked for slaughter we might as well clip your ears straight away, and save yourself some trouble."

"I would very much like to try all the same," said Espen, and he was given permission to do so.

He took the axe out of his knapsack and fitted it into the haft again.

"Now chop away," he said to the axe, and it chopped so that the wood chips flew around and it wasn't long before the oak tree fell to the ground. That done, Espen took out his spade and fitted it to the handle.

"Now dig away," he said, and it began to dig and delve so that soil and rock flew around and soon the well was dug. When it was as deep and wide as he wanted he took out the walnut and set it in a corner at the bottom of the well and removed the plug of moss.

"Now trickle and run," he said, and it began to run so that the water gushed out of the hole and in a short time the well was brim-full.

Espen Ash Lad had cut down the oak tree that overshadowed the king's windows and made a well in the courtyard, so he won the princess and half the kingdom, just as the king had promised.

But it was just as well that Peter and Paul had lost their ears, otherwise they would have had to hear every time someone said Espen wasn't so crazy after all with all his wonderings.

The Princess on the Glass Mountain

There was once a man who owned a meadow which lay high up on the hillside and on this meadow stood a hayloft which he had built to store his hay. But, sad to say, there had not been much hay in the barn in the past few years because every St John's Eve, when the grass stood very green and lush, the meadow was eaten to the ground as if a whole flock of sheep had been there munching away during the night.

This happened once and it happened twice and the man had had enough of this so he said to his sons, "Can you believe it?" He had three sons and the third one was nicknamed Ash Lad and the man decided that one of them had to go and sleep in the barn on St John's Eve because it was too much to bear that the grass should be eaten again right down to the roots just as it had been in the last two years. So he said whoever went must keep a sharp lookout.

Well, the oldest son was willing to go to guard the meadow. He was quite sure that he could keep an eye on the grass – neither man nor beast, not even the devil himself, would get anywhere near it. So, when evening came he set off to the barn and lay down to sleep, but a short while into the night there was such a loud crashing noise, like an earthquake, and the walls and the roof shook. The lad leapt up and took to his heels as fast as he could, and not once did he dare to look back. And so during the night the grass was eaten up just as it had been in the previous years.

On the next St John's Eve the man said again that it was too

81

*Ash Lad goes to the barn to guard the hay crop by Erik
Werenskiold. Illustration © O. Væring Eftf. AS.*

distressing that all the grass in the meadow should be lost year after year, so one of the sons must go and guard it – and guard it well too. So the second oldest son was willing to try what he could do and off he went to the hayloft where he lay down to sleep just as his brother had done. But during the night there came such a crash, like an earthquake, even worse than on the previous St John's Eve. When the lad heard this he was so scared that he ran off as fast as if he was being paid for it.

The next year it was Ash Lad's turn; but when he was getting ready to go the other two laughed and mocked him, saying, "Oh yes! You're just the one to guard the hay; you who have never learned anything except to sit among the ashes and toast yourself!" But Ash Lad took no notice of this tittle-tattle and when it came towards evening he set off up the hill to the outlying meadow. There he went inside the hayloft and lay down, but after a while the barn began to groan and creak so that it was frightening to hear.

"Well," Ash Lad said to himself, "if it gets no worse than this then I can cope with it."

A short time later there was another crash which brought the hay showering down on the lad.

"Oh well," he thought, "If it doesn't get any worse than this then I can cope with it." But just then there came a third rumble followed by an earthquake and Ash Lad thought the walls and the roof were about to collapse, but soon it was over and everything became as quiet as the grave.

"I expect it will come again," thought Ash Lad.

But no, it didn't come again. It was quiet and it remained quiet. When he had been lying down a little longer he heard a sound like a horse standing just outside the barn door chewing at the grass. He crept to the door to see what it was, and there stood a horse munching away. Ash Lad had never seen such a big, fat and splendid horse before; and by its side there lay a saddle and a bridle and a full suit of armour for a knight, all made of copper and so polished that the light shone from them.

"Aha!" Ash Lad said to himself, "so it's you who eats up all our hay. I'll soon put a stop to that."

He lost no time in finding the steel from his tinder-box and threw it over the horse so that it had no strength to stir from the spot and it became so tame that the lad could do what he liked with it.* He mounted it and rode off to a place that no-one knew of and there he left it safe.

When he got home his brothers laughed and asked how things had gone with him saying, "You certainly didn't spend much time lying in the barn, even if you managed to get as far as that."

"I lay in the barn until the sun rose but I neither heard nor saw anything," said Ash Lad, "I can't think what it was that you were so afraid of!"

"In that case, we'll go and see just how well you guarded the grass," the brothers replied. So when they arrived, there was the grass standing as deep and lush as it had been on the previous evening.

On the next St John's Eve it was the same story. Neither of the two older brothers dared go off to the distant meadow to guard the crop, but Ash Lad was not afraid to go, and everything happened in the same way as on the previous St John's Eve. First there was a crash and an earthquake, followed by another and then another; but all three earthquakes were much stronger this time. Then all became as quiet as the grave and

---

*Tinder boxes had long been endowed with magical properties in Norse mythology but it was Hans Andersen's tale *The Tinder Box* (1835) which attracted most attention. *The tale of The Princess on the Glass Hill* appeared in the collection by Asbjørnsen and Moe ten years later.

the lad heard something chewing outside the barn door.

He crept to the door as quietly as he could – and yes! there was another horse standing by the wall and munching away, and it was much bigger and fatter than the one before; and a saddle sat on its back and there was a bridle too and a full suit of armour for a knight – and all made of shining silver and as fine as you would wish to see.

"Aha!" said the lad to himself. "It's you, is it, who is eating up all our hay during the night? I'll soon put a stop to that." He found the steel from his tinder box and threw it over the horse's mane and then it stood there as meek as a lamb. So, the lad rode this horse too to the place where he kept the other one and then he went home again.

"Can we take it that there's a fine crop out in the hay meadow today?" said one of the brothers.

"Oh yes! There is indeed," said Ash Lad.

Of course they had to go off and see, and there stood the grass deep and lush as it had been the year before; but they were not any kinder to Ash Lad even so.

When the next St John's Eve came round neither of the two older brothers had the courage to go and lie in the barn and keep an eye on the grass, for they had been so thoroughly scared on the night they lay there that they had never forgotten it. But Ash Lad was not afraid to go and the same things happened as on the two previous St John's Eves – there were three earthquakes, each one worse than the one before, and during the last one the lad was thrown from one wall of the barn to the other; but suddenly all was as quiet as the grave.

When he had remained resting for a little while he heard something chewing outside the barn door; once again he crept over to the barn door and there stood a horse just outside, much bigger and fatter than the two others he had captured before, and with both saddle and bridle and a full suit of armour made of pure, red gold.

"Aha!" said the lad to himself. "It's you is it this time eating up our hay? I'll soon put a stop to that." So he pulled out his tinder steel and threw it over the horse which then stood as if it was nailed to the ground and the lad could do just as he pleased with it. He rode off to the place where he kept the other two and then went home again. There the two brothers mocked him as they did before. They said they could see he had kept a good watch on the grass that night because he looked as if he was still sleep-walking. But Ash Lad took no notice; he merely said that they should go and see for themselves. This they did and there stood the grass as deep and lush as it had been before.

The king of the country where Ash Lad lived had a daughter whom he said he would only give to the man who could ride to the top of the glass mountain – this was a very high hill made of glass, as smooth and slippery as ice, near the king's manor. On the very top of this hill the king's daughter would sit with three golden apples in her lap, and the man who could ride up and take the three golden apples should have the Princess and half the kingdom.

The king had this posted in all the churches throughout the land and in many other kingdoms too. The king's daughter was so beautiful that everyone who saw her could not help losing their hearts to her, and so it is not surprising that all the princes and knights were eager to win her and half the kingdom too. And so they came riding from every part of the world, all gorgeously arrayed, and on magnificent prancing horses, and there wasn't one of them who didn't believe that he, and only he, would win the king's daughter.

So when the day came that the king had set, there was such a crush of knights and princes by the glass hill that it made one feel giddy, and anyone who could walk or even crawl was

The princess on the Glass Mountain, by Theodor Kittelsen.

there to see who would win the king's daughter. Ash Lad's two brothers were also there but they flatly refused to have him with them for, they said, people would mock them if they were seen in the company of such a dimwit, scruffy and dirty as he was from sitting poking in the ashes.

"In that case I can just as well go by myself, it's all the same to me," said Ash Lad.

When the two brothers arrived at the glass hill, all the princes and knights were riding their horses so hard that they were covered in sweat, but it was all to no purpose, for as soon as the horses had set foot on the hill they slipped and not one of them could get more than a few metres up the hill. This was no great surprise for the hill was as smooth as a sheet of glass and as steep as a house wall. But they were all so keen to win the king's daughter and half the kingdom that they rode and they slipped again and again.

At last all the horses were so worn out that they could do no more, and in such a lather that the foam dripped off them, and so the knights had to give up. The king was just thinking that he would announce that the trial would continue the next day to see if they could do any better, when suddenly a knight appeared riding a horse so magnificent that no-one had ever seen such a horse before: it had copper armour and a copper bridle so brightly polished that the light shone from them.

The others called out to him that he might as well save himself the trouble of trying to ride up the glass hill because it would all come to nothing. But he paid no attention to them, he just set his horse at the hill and went up easily enough for probably a third of the way and then he turned his horse round and rode down again. But the king's daughter thought she had never before seen such a handsome knight, and while he was riding she sat and prayed that he would reach the top.

When she saw him turning his horse she threw one of the

golden apples after him and it rolled down into his shoe. But when he had reached the bottom of the hill he rode off so fast that no-one could tell what had become of him. That evening all the princes and knights appeared before the king, and the knight who had managed to ride so far up the glass hill was asked to show the golden apple that the king's daughter had thrown; but none of them had anything to show. One after another they came but no-one was able to show the apple.

In the evening Ash Lad's brothers came home too and told a long story about riding up the glass hill. At first, they said, there was not one who could ride up more than a single step.

"But then there came someone who had copper armour and a copper bridle all so polished that the light shone from them as far as one could see. He was a fellow who really knew how to ride! He rode over a third of the way up the glass hill and he could easily have ridden the whole way up if he had wanted to, but he turned round, perhaps thinking that was enough for a first attempt."

"Oh! I would like to have seen him!" said Ash Lad who sat by the hearth and poked about in the ashes as he usually did.

"Oh! You would, would you?" his brothers mocked him. "You hardly look as if you are fit to be in the company of such important men, you scruffy creature sitting there among the ashes."

On the next day the brothers were keen to set off again and Ash Lad again begged them to let him go with them to see those who were riding; but no, they said, there was no likelihood of that. He was far too scruffy and dirty.

"Oh well," Ash Lad replied, "I'll just have to go alone, all by myself, that's what I'll do."

When the brothers arrived at the glass hill the princes and knights were beginning to ride again, and you can be sure that they had seen to it that their horses were newly shod. But that didn't help. They rode and they slipped just as they had done the day before and none of them came any further than a few metres up the hill, and when they had worn out their horses so that they could not do any more, they all had to give up.

The king was thinking that he would announce that the riding should take place for the last time on the following day to see if it all went better then. Then he had second thoughts. He would wait a little to see if the knight in copper armour would come on this day too. They saw nothing of him until suddenly someone appeared riding a horse which was far, far grander than the one the knight in copper armour had ridden, and this knight had silver armour and a silver saddle and a silver bridle, all so bright that the light sparkled and glinted from them from far away.

The others shouted out to him saying that it was not worth his while to try to ride up the glass hill for it would never be of any use. But the knight took no notice of them. He rode straight at the glass hill and went up even further than the knight in the copper armour had done, but when he had gone two-thirds of the way up he turned his horse round and rode down again. The princess liked him even better and she sat and wished that he would manage to come right to the top, but when she saw him turn and ride down again she threw the second apple after him and it rolled down into his shoe. But as soon as he had reached the bottom of the glass hill he rode off so fast that no-one could see what became of him.

In the evening when everyone had to appear before the king and the princess so that the one who had the golden apple could show it, they came one after the other but no-one had any golden apples to show. So, as on the day before, the two brothers went home and told how the day had gone and how all had ridden at the hill but none had made it to the top.

"But at last," they said, "a knight arrived in a silver suit of armour and he also had a silver saddle and a silver bridle, and he could certainly ride – he got as far as two-thirds of the way up the hill and then he turned back. He was a fine fellow he was! And the Princess threw the second apple to him."

"Oh! I would like to have seen him," said Ash Lad.

"Oh yes!" his brothers said. "Perhaps you think his armour was as bright as the ashes you sit and poke about in, you scruffy dirty creature!"

On the third day everything happened just as it had on the other days: Ash Lad wanted to go along and see the riding but the other two refused to have him with them. When they came to the glass hill there was no-one who could get as far as two metres up it. Everyone was now waiting for the knight in silver armour but there was neither sight nor sound of him.

At last someone came riding a horse so magnificent that no-one had ever seen one like it. The knight had a suit of armour of gold, a gold saddle and a gold bridle, so splendidly polished that the light gleamed and sparkled from it from far away. The other knights and princes were so struck with amazement when they saw how grand he was that they didn't even call to him that there was no point in trying to ride up the hill. He rode straight at the glass hill and flew up like a feather in a gust of wind so that the Princess didn't even have time to wish that he would get right to the top.

As soon as he reached the top he took the third golden apple from the Princess's lap, turned his horse and rode down again. Then no sooner was he down than he disappeared out of sight in the blink of an eye.

Now, when the two brothers came home that evening, they had a long story to tell how the riding had gone that day and finally they had much to say about the knight in the golden armour. "He was a fine fellow he was," they said. "Such a great knight isn't to be found in the whole wide world."

"Oh! How I should like to have seen him!" said Ash Lad.

"Oh yes!" his brothers replied. "Those ashes you idly poke about in don't shine nearly as brightly, you scruffy, dirty creature!"

On the next day all the knights and princes were to present themselves before the king and his daughter – it was probably too late on the evening before – so that whoever had the golden apple could reveal it, but one after another they came, first the princes and then the knights, and none of them had a golden apple.

"Well," said the king, "someone must have it. We all saw that someone rode up and took it." So he ordered that everyone in the kingdom should come to the palace and see if they could produce the golden apple. Well, they all came, one after the other, but no-one had the golden apple, and at long last the two brothers of Ash Lad appeared. They were the last and the king asked if there really was no-one else in the kingdom.

"Oh! Well, we do have a brother," they said, "but he certainly didn't take the golden apple; he hasn't moved from the fireplace ashes on any of the three days."

"Even so," said the king, "everyone else has been to the manor-house so he should come too." So Ash Lad too had to go up to the king's manor.

The king asked him, "Now, speak up, have you got the golden apple?"

"Yes, I have," said Ash Lad. "Here is the first one, and here is the second, and here is the third one as well." And he took all three golden apples out of his pocket, and at the same time he cast aside his sooty rags and stood before them in his golden armour which shone so brightly that the light gleamed from him.

"Well!" said the king, "You shall have my daughter and half my kingdom. You fully deserve both of them."

So there was a wedding and Ash Lad married the king's daughter and, you may be sure, there were great celebrations; for everyone was invited, even those who had not been able to ride to the top of the glass hill, and if the celebrations are not yet over then they are still going on.

The Golden Castle that Hung in the Air

There was once a man who had three sons. When he died, the two eldest decided to go out into the world to try their luck; but they wouldn't have the youngest one with them at any price. They said, "As for you, you're good for nothing but to sit and hold the pine torches and poke about among the ashes and blow on the embers."

"Ah well, in that case I'll just have to go by myself," said Espen Ash Lad. "At least I'll not fall out with those with me."

The two of them set off and, after travelling for several days, they came to a great forest. There they sat down to rest and eat the food they had brought, for they were tired and hungry. As they sat there an old woman suddenly appeared from a tussock and begged for a little food. She was so old and frail that her mouth quivered and her head nodded and she had to support herself with a stick.

She said she had not had a morsel to eat for a hundred years; but the two lads just laughed and carried on eating, saying that if she hadn't eaten for such a long time she could almost certainly hold out for the rest of her life without eating up any of their food. They said they didn't have much food anyway, and they had none to spare.

When they had eaten their fill and could eat no more, they rested a while and then set out again. At long last they came to the king's manor where they both obtained work.

A short time after they had left home Ash Lad gathered

together the food his brothers had cast aside and put it in his little knapsack. He also took the old gun which had no lock; he thought it might come in useful along the way. Then he set out.

After he had walked for several days he came to the great forest through which his brothers had passed. When he felt hungry and tired he sat down under a tree to rest and have a little to eat. But he kept his eyes open and as he was opening up his knapsack he caught sight of a picture hanging on a tree. It was a painting of a young girl or a princess who was so beautiful that he couldn't take his eyes off her. He forgot both food and knapsack and took down the picture and just sat there gazing at it.

Suddenly the old woman appeared out of the tussock, her mouth quivering, her head nodding, and hobbling along with a stick. She begged for a little food because, she said, she hadn't had a morsel of food in her mouth for a hundred years.

"Then it's high time you had a little to eat, old grandmother," said Espen, and he gave her some of the breadcrumbs he had.

The old woman said that no-one had called her 'mother' for a hundred years and she said she would certainly do him a favour in return. She gave him a ball of grey wool which he had only to roll in front of him and he would come to wherever he wished. But he shouldn't trouble himself with the picture; she said that would only bring him bad luck. Ash Lad thought that was all very well but he wouldn't go without the picture, so he tucked it under his arm and rolled the ball of wool in front of him.

It was not long before he reached the king's manor where his brothers had obtained work. Ash Lad also asked to be given work but they replied that they had no use for him for they had recently taken on two other servants. However, Ash

Lad begged so earnestly that in the end he was allowed to help the Master of the Horse and learn all about grooming and looking after horses, something Ash Lad was very happy to do for he was fond of horses.

He was quick and clever at his work and it wasn't long before everyone at the king's manor became fond of him. But whenever he had time to spare he would go and gaze at the painting which he had hung in a corner of the hayloft.

His brothers were idle and lazy and so they were often in trouble and folk at the manor-house spoke ill of them. When they saw that Ash Lad fared better than they did, they became jealous and told the Master of the Horse that he worshipped idols and that he prayed to a picture and not to Our Lord. Even though the Master of the Horse thought highly of Ash Lad, it wasn't long before he told the king what he had heard. But the king only snapped sharply at him: for he was always so sad and depressed since his daughters had been carried off by a troll. However, they dinned the tale into the king's ears for so long that in the end he just had to find out what the lad was up to.

When he went up to the hayloft and set eyes on the picture he saw that it was a portrait of his youngest daughter. When Ash Lad's brothers heard this they were ready at once with another story, telling the Master of the Horse that their brother had said that he knew how he could get the king's daughter back. It wasn't long before the Master of the Horse went to the king with this story; and when the king heard of it he called for Ash Lad and said, "Your brothers say that you can bring my daughter back, and now you must do it."

Ash Lad replied that he didn't even know it was the king's daughter before the king himself had said so but if he could rescue her and bring her back he would certainly do his best but he would need two days to make arrangements and fit himself out. This he was allowed to have.

When he was ready he took out the ball of grey wool and threw it down on the road and it rolled and rolled and Ash Lad followed it until he came to the old woman who had given it to him. He asked her what he should do and she said he must take his old gun and three hundred cases of spikes and horse-shoe nails, and three hundred barrels of barley, and three hundred barrels of groats, and three hundred butchered pigs, and three hundred ox carcasses, and then he should roll the ball of wool in front of him until he met a raven and a troll-child. He would then be sure to find his way for those two were part of her family.

So Ash Lad did as she said. He returned to the manor house to get his old gun and to ask the king for spikes and beef and pork; and for horses, men and carts to transport them. The king thought it was a great deal to ask but if he could get his daughter back, he said he could have everything he wanted, even if it was half the kingdom.

When the lad was ready to set off he again rolled the ball of wool along the road and he hadn't gone for many days before he came to a high mountain and there, on the mountain, high in a fir tree, sat a raven. Ash Lad walked on until he was right under the fir tree and he began to take aim with his gun.

"No! Don't shoot! Don't shoot me and I'll help you!" shrieked the raven.

"I've never heard of anyone praising roast raven," said Ash Lad, "and since you're so afraid for your life I can just as well spare it."

So he lowered his gun and the raven came flying down and said, "Up on the mountain is a troll child who is lost and can't find his way down again. I shall help you get up there so that you can take the youngster home and so get a reward which you will certainly have a use for. When you get there the troll will offer you the finest things he has, but you should have nothing to do with them. You must take nothing but the little grey donkey which stands behind the stable door.

So the raven took Ash Lad on its back and flew up on to the mountain with him and set him down there. When he had wandered about for a while he heard the troll child whimpering and wailing because he couldn't find his way down again.

Ash Lad talked to him kindly and they were soon on friendly terms with each other. He said he would help him down the mountain and take him home to the troll's house so that he wouldn't get lost on the way. Then they went to the raven which took them both on its back and carried them all the way to the troll's mountain home.

When the troll set eyes on his child again he was so full of joy that he quite forgot himself and invited Ash Lad to come in with him and take whatever he would like because he had rescued his son. The troll offered him gold and silver and many fine and costly things but the lad said he would rather have a horse. Yes, he should have a horse, said the troll, and off they went to the stable which was full of the finest horses whose coats gleamed like the sun and the moon. But Ash Lad thought they were all too big for him, so he had a look behind the stable door and he caught sight of the little, grey donkey standing there.

"That's the one I would like," he said. "That would suit me fine. If I fall off, I'll not have very far to fall to the ground."

The troll was not at all keen to lose his donkey but, since he had said that Ash Lad could have whatever he wanted, he had to stand by it. So the lad got the donkey, together with the saddle and bridle and everything that went with it, and he then hurried on his way.

They travelled through forest and field, over mountains and vast moorlands, and when they had gone further than far the donkey asked Ash Lad if he could see anything.

"No," he replied, "I can see nothing but a high mountain that looks blue in the distance."

"Well, we have to pass right through that mountain," said the donkey.

"Am I supposed to believe that?" asked Espen Ash Lad.

As they approached the mountain a unicorn came charging at them as if it intended to eat them alive.

"Now, that makes me feel afraid," said Ash Lad.

"There's no need to be," said the donkey. "Just unload two score of ox carcasses and ask the unicorn to bore a hole in the mountain to break a way through for us."

Ash Lad did as the donkey had said and when the unicorn had eaten all it could, they promised it a couple of score of butchered pigs if only it would go ahead and bore a hole in the mountain so that they could get through. When it heard that, the unicorn bored the hole and broke a way through the mountain so fast that it was all they could do to keep up with it. When it had finished they threw it a couple of score of pig carcasses and then, when they were through the mountain, they travelled a long way across many lands, and once again through forests and fields, and over fells and wild moorlands.

"Do you see anything now?" asked the donkey.

"I can see only the sky and wild mountains," said the lad. They went on again, further than far, and as they came higher the mountain landscape became more level and flatter so they could see further round them.

"Do you see anything now?" asked the donkey.

"Yes," said Ash Lad, "I can see something far, far away. It glitters and twinkles like a little star."

"It's not as little as it seems to be," said the donkey.

When they had travelled on, further than far again, the donkey asked, "Do you see anything now?"

"Yes," said Ash Lad, "now I can see something a long way

away. It shines like a moon."

"That's no moon," the donkey said. "That's the silver castle we are heading for. When we get there we shall see three dragons lying on guard by the gate. They have not been awake for a hundred years so moss has grown over their eyes.

"Oh! I think I shall be afraid of them," said Ash Lad.

"Oh, no! There's no need to be afraid," said the donkey.

"You must wake up the youngest dragon and throw into its jaws two score of ox carcasses and butchered pigs and then I expect it will talk to the other two and you will be allowed to enter the castle."

They travelled far, and further than far, before they reached the castle which was large and splendid and everything they saw was made of silver. The dragons lay outside the gate and blocked the way so that no-one could enter, but it had all been quiet and peaceful and they hadn't had much to do on their watch, and they were so overgrown with moss that no-one could tell what they were made of; and alongside them small trees had begun to grow among the moss.

Ash Lad woke up the smallest dragon and it rubbed its eyes and scraped away the moss. When the dragon saw that there were people nearby it came at them with its jaws wide open but Ash Lad was ready for it and he tossed ox carcasses and pigs down its gullet until it had eaten all it could, and then it became more reasonable to talk to. He asked it to wake up the other dragons and tell them to move out of the way so that he could enter the castle; but the dragon said it dared not and would not do that because they had not been awake or had any food to eat for a hundred years and it was afraid they would be raving mad and gobble up everything living or dead.

Ash Lad said there was no need to worry about that. They would leave behind a hundred ox carcasses and a hundred butchered pigs and then go away for a while. The dragons could then eat their fill and come to their senses by the time they returned. Yes, the dragon agreed to that.

But before the dragons were properly awake and had got the moss out of their eyes they rushed around in a daze snapping at all and sundry. All the youngest dragon could do was to keep out of their way until they found the scent of the meat. Then they gobbled up whole oxen and pig carcasses and ate until they were full; then they became more docile and good-natured and allowed Ash Lad to go into the castle.

There he found everything was so splendid that he had never imagined there could be anywhere so magnificent. But there was nobody there. He went from room to room and opened all the doors but he saw no-one. At last he peeped through the door of a room he had not seen before and inside sat a princess spinning.

She was so pleased and happy when she caught sight of him, "Good gracious!" she exclaimed, "can it really be that Christian folk dare to come here? But you had better go away again, otherwise the troll will kill you. A troll with three heads lives here."

But Ash Lad said he wasn't going to go away even if the troll had seven heads.

When the princess heard that, she wanted him to try to wield the great, rusty sword which hung behind the door, but, no, he was unable to wield it – he couldn't even lift it.

"Well," said the princess, "If you can't manage to lift it, you'll have to take a drink from the flask that hangs beside it. That's what the troll does when he goes out to use it."

Ash Lad took a couple of swigs and then he could wield the sword as easily as if it were a pastry board. Just at that moment the troll came blustering in.

"Phew!" he shrieked, "what a smell of Christian blood there is in here!"

"So there is," said Ash Lad, "but there's no need to snort like that. You won't have to put up with that smell any longer." And with that he cut off all the troll's three heads.

At first the princess was so happy, just as if she had been given something really wonderful, but after a while she became down-hearted as she pined for her sister who had been carried off by a troll with six heads and was now in a golden castle three hundred miles beyond the world's end. Ash Lad didn't see this as any great problem: he could go and fetch both the princess and the castle.

He took the sword and the flask, mounted the donkey and ordered the dragons to follow him and carry the beef, the pork and the spikes.

When they had travelled for some time, journeying over land and strand for a long, long way, the donkey said, "Can you see anything?"

"I can see nothing but land, water, sky and high mountains," said Ash Lad.

So they travelled on, further than far, and then the donkey asked again, "Do you see anything now?"

Ash Lad looked carefully into the distance and then he said he could see something far, far away which shone like a tiny star.

"It is sure to get bigger," said the donkey, and they journeyed on again for a long, long way until the donkey asked once more, "Do you see anything now?"

"Now it's shining like a moon," Ash Lad said.

"That's good," replied the donkey, and on they went again, further than far, over land and strand, over mountain and moorland, until the donkey asked once more, "Do you see anything now?"

"Now I think it is shining like the sun," said Ash Lad.

"That's it," said the donkey. "That is the golden castle we

The princess and the spinning wheel, by Erik Werenskiold.
Illustration © O. Væring Eftf. AS.

are going to. But outside the castle there is a man-eating serpent barring the way and keeping guard."

"I think I shall be afraid of that," said Ash Lad.

"No, there's no need to be afraid," said the donkey. "We'll pile layers of twigs over it and among them we'll put plenty of horseshoe nails and set fire to it. Then we shall be rid of it."

At long last they came to the castle that hung in the air but the man-eating serpent was lying in front of it barring the way. Ash Lad gave the dragons a good feed of ox and pig carcasses so that they would help him and then they spread over the serpent a pile of twigs and layers of spikes and horseshoe nails until they had used up all the three hundred crates they had brought with them. When they had done that they set fire to it and burned the serpent alive.

When all that was done, one of the dragons flew underneath the castle and lifted it up, while the other two flew high into the sky to release the chains from the hooks they hung on and lowered the castle to the ground.

Ash Lad went inside and discovered that everything was even more splendid than in the silver castle, but he saw no-one until he came to the innermost room and there he found the princess lying on a golden bed. She was sleeping so soundly that it seemed as if she were dead. She was not dead although he couldn't wake her up. Her face was red and white like milk and blood.

While Ash Lad stood there gazing at her the troll came rushing in. He had scarcely put his first head through the doorway before he shrieked, "Phew! What a smell of Christian blood there is in here!"

"That's quite likely," said Ash Lad, "but there's no need to puff and blow so loudly about it. You won't be troubled by it for long," and with that he cut off all the troll's heads as if they were growing on a cabbage stalk. Then the dragons put the castle on their backs and flew home with it and set it down beside the silver castle and there it shone all round, far and wide.

When the princess from the silver castle went to the window in the morning and caught sight of the golden castle she was so happy that she ran over to it straight away; but when she saw her sister lying there sleeping as if she were dead she told Ash Lad that they would not be able to bring her back to life before they had fetched the Waters of Life and Death which were to be found in two wells on either side of a golden castle hanging in the air nine hundred miles beyond the world's end, and this was where the third sister lived.

There's no help for it, then, Ash Lad thought. He would have to go and fetch that castle too. It wasn't long before he was on his way and he travelled far, and further than far, through many kingdoms, through fields and forests, across mountains and beaches, over land and water. At last he reached the world's end, and still he and the faithful donkey travelled on, far and long, over heath and hill and high mountains.

One day the donkey asked, "Do you see anything?"

"I see nothing but heaven and earth," said the lad.

A few days later the donkey asked again, "Do you see anything now?"

"Yes," the lad replied. "Now I think I can glimpse something high up and far away. It looks like a tiny star."

"It's probably not so tiny, though," said the donkey.

When they had travelled on a while longer the donkey asked again, "Do you see anything now?"

"Yes, now I think it shines like a moon."

"That's good," said the donkey."

So, on they travelled for a few days more, "Do you see anything now?" asked the donkey.

"Yes," Ash Lad replied. "Now it shines like the sun."

"That is where we are going," said the donkey. "That is the golden castle that hangs in the air; and that is where the princess lives who was carried off by a troll with nine heads. But all the wild animals in the world lie on guard there and bar the way in."

"Huff!" said Ash Lad. "Now I think I will be afraid."

"Oh no! there's no need to be afraid said the donkey and explained that there was no danger as long as he didn't linger about but left as soon as he had filled his pitchers with the water. It was only possible to go there for one hour during the day and that began at noon. If he didn't finish what he had to do and get away in that time, then the wild animals would tear him into a thousand pieces.

"Yes," Ash Lad replied. He would manage that and he certainly wouldn't hang about too long.

It was twelve o'clock when they arrived at the castle, and there were all the wild and savage animals that ever lived lying like a wall in front of the gate and on both sides of the road. But they slept like logs and stones and not one of them so much as lifted a paw. Ash Lad passed between them taking great care not to tread on their toes or the tips of their tails. He filled his pitchers with the Waters of Life and Death and while he did this he cast an eye over the castle which was built of pure gold. It was the most splendid he had ever seen and he guessed it must be even grander inside.

"Pooh!" he muttered to himself, "I've plenty of time. I can easily look around for half an hour."

So he opened the door and went in. Inside the castle everything was grander than grand. He went from one magnificent room to another, everywhere was adorned with gold and pearls and everything that was most costly in the world, but he saw no sign of any people.

Finally, he came to a chamber where a princess lay sleeping on a golden bed as though she were dead. She appeared as elegant as the finest queen and as red and white as blood and snow; and she was so beautiful that he had never seen anything so beautiful except her picture – for she it was whose portrait was painted there. Ash Lad forgot both the water he had come to fetch, and the wild animals and the entire castle; he had eyes only for the princess. He thought he could never have enough of gazing at her, but she slept as if she were dead, and he was unable to wake her.

Towards evening the troll came rushing in crashing and banging all the gates and doors so that the whole castle rattled.

"Phuff," he said, "it smells of Christian flesh in here," and he stuck his first head through the door and sniffed the air.

"I dare say it does," said Ash Lad, "but there's no need to puff and blow about it as if you're going to burst, because you won't be troubled with that smell much longer." And with that he cut off all the troll's nine heads. But when he had done that he felt so tired that he couldn't keep his eyes open. So he lay down on the bed beside the princess and all the time she slept, night and day, as if she would never wake again, but at about midnight she woke up for a moment and told him that he had set her free but she had to remain there for three more years. If she didn't come home then, he must come and fetch her.

He didn't wake up until it was one o'clock the following day and then he heard the donkey braying and making a fuss, so he thought he had better set off for home. But first of all, he cut a piece out of the princess's dress to take with him. With one thing and another he had lingered there so long that the animals were beginning to wake up and rouse themselves. By the time Ash Lad had mounted the donkey they had formed a ring round him and things looked really menacing. The donkey told him to sprinkle a few drops of the Water of Death on them. This he did and they all fell down on the spot and never moved a limb again.

On the way home the donkey said, "I expect when you have gained honour and glory you will forget me and everything I have done for you and hunger will force me to my knees."

"No, that will never happen," Ash Lad assured him.

When he arrived back with the Water of Life the princess sprinkled a few drops on her sister and she woke up. And there was great joy and happiness.

Then they went home to the king and he too was full of joy and happiness to have his two daughters back again. But he also longed for the three years to pass so that his youngest daughter could come home too. He made the lad who had rescued the two princesses a mighty man so that he was first in the land after the king; but there were many who were jealous because he had become so important. One of them was known as the Red Knight who, it was said, wished to have the oldest princess. He got her to sprinkle a few drops of the Water of Death over Ash Lad and he fell into a deep sleep.

When three years and part of a fourth had passed a foreign warship came sailing in and on board was the third princess and she had with her a three-year old child. She sent a message up to the king's palace that she would not set foot on land until they sent to the ship the man who had come to the golden castle and set her free. So they sent one of the most important men at the court and when he met the princess on board the ship he removed his hat and bowed and knelt before her.

"Can this man be your father, my son?" the princess asked the child, who was playing with a golden apple.

"No," the child replied. "My father doesn't crawl around like a cheese maggot."

So they sent another man of the same rank and this time it

was the Red Knight, but he fared no better than the first one, and the princess sent him back with the message that if they didn't send the right man, they would be in serious trouble. When they heard this they had to wake up Ash Lad with the Water of Life and he went down to the ship to meet the princess. He didn't make much of a bow; he merely nodded his head and brought out the piece of material he had cut from the princess's dress in the golden castle.

"That's my father," the child shouted, and gave him the golden apple he had been playing with.

Then there was great rejoicing over the whole kingdom. The old king was the happiest of them all because he had his favourite child again. One day it came to light what the Red Knight and the oldest princess had done to Ash Lad, and the king ordered that they should both be rolled around in spiked barrels, but Ash Lad and the youngest princess pleaded for them and they were spared.

One day just before they were to celebrate the wedding at the palace, Ash Lad stood looking out of the window. Spring had arrived and they were letting out the horses and cattle; the last to come out of the stable was the donkey but it was so starved of food that it had to crawl through the door on its knees.

Ash Lad felt so ashamed of himself for having forgotten about the donkey that he went down but was at a loss to know what he could do to help. The donkey said that the best thing he could do would be to cut off its head. He was not willing to do this but the donkey pleaded so earnestly that in the end he had to do it. At the very moment that the head fell to the ground the troll's spell which had been cast over it was broken, and there stood the most handsome prince anyone could imagine.

He had the second princess for his wife and they celebrated

with a wedding feast which was the talk of seven kingdoms.

Then they built themselves houses
And made themselves shoes
And had many small princes
In ones and in twos.

Ash Lad and Colfox*

Once upon a time there was a king who had hundreds of sheep and hundreds of goats and cattle. He also had hundreds of horses and great heaps of gold and silver. But even so he was so down-hearted that he never wished to meet anyone, much less talk to anyone. He had been like this ever since he had lost his youngest daughter, and life would have been difficult enough for him even if he had not lost her, for there was a troll who made so much noise and disturbance that folk no longer wished to come to the king's manor-house.

Every now and then the troll let out all the horses and they trampled down the meadows and corn fields and ate up all the crops. Sometimes he tore off the heads of the king's ducks and geese and at other times he killed the cows in their stalls; and sometimes he drove the sheep and goats over the crag; and every time folk went to fish in the pond they found all the fish had been driven on to dry land and were lying there dead.

Now, there was an elderly couple who had three sons; the first was called Peter, the second was called Paul, and the third

---

* The original title to this tale is *Rødrev og Askeladden* 'Redfox and the Ash Lad' which is sometimes translated as 'Ash Lad and Mr Glibtongue.' A reference to the colfox would seem to be more appropriate – a species of fox with black tips on its ears and tail, and referred to by Geoffrey Chaucer in his *Canterbury Tales* as being 'ful of sly iniquitee', an apt description of the character of Rødrev in this story. Colfox is recorded as a surname in 13th century Assize Rolls: Redfox is not recorded.

had the name Espen Ash Lad because he was always lounging about poking among the ashes. They were reliable sons but Peter, who was the oldest, was regarded as the most reliable. He asked his father for permission to go out into the world and seek his fortune.

"Yes, certainly you can have permission," said his father. "Better late than never, my son!"

He was given brandy in a flask and food in his knapsack and he lost no time in setting off down the hill.

When he had walked for some time he came across an old woman lying by the roadside.

"Oh, my dear boy, give me a little morsel of food," she pleaded.

But Peter hardly gave her a glance; he just tossed his head and went on his way.

"Ah well," said the old woman, "you just go, and you shall see what happens."

Peter walked on and on, further than far, until he came to the king's manor-house and there stood the king on the balcony feeding the hens.

"Good evening and God bless you," said Peter.

"Chuck, chuck, chick, chick," the king called, and scattered corn east and west but took not the slightest notice of Peter.

"Right!" said Peter to himself. "You just stand there and scatter corn and cackle to the chickens until you turn into a bear. You needn't bother listening to what I have to say."

So he walked into the kitchen and seated himself on a bench as if he were some important man.

"What sort of little whippersnapper are you?" asked the cook. Peter, who had not yet grown a beard, thought this was mockery and insulting and he began to give the cook a beating but just at that moment in walked the king and cut three red stripes from the boy's back and the cook rubbed salt in the wounds. They then sent him home by the same way he had come.

No sooner had Peter arrived home than Paul wanted to set out too. So, he also was given some brandy in a flask and some food in his knapsack and he lost no time in setting off down the hill.

When he had gone some way along the road he came across the old woman who begged for food but he strode right past and made not the slightest reply. At the king's manor nothing went one jot better for him than it had for Peter; the king only said 'chick, chick' and the cook called him an ill-mannered little brat, and he was about to give her a beating when the king walked in with a butcher's knife and cut three red stripes from his back and rubbed hot embers in. They then sent him on his way home with a sore back.

Then Ash Lad crept out of the cinders and began to bestir himself. On the first day he shook all the ashes off himself, the next day he washed himself and combed his hair and on the third day he dressed in his Sunday best.

"I say! Take a look at that!" said Peter. "We have a new sun shining here now. I guess you're planning to go to the king's manor to win a princess and half a kingdom! You might just as well stay among the ashes and lounge around among the cinders."

But Ash Lad was deaf in that ear. He went to see his father and asked for permission to go out into the world.

"Whatever can you do out in the world?" asked the old man. "Things didn't go well with either Peter or Paul so how on earth will they go with you, eh?

But Ash Lad didn't give up and before long he did get permission to go.

His brothers didn't want him to be given any food or drink to take with him but his mother gave him the rind from a cheese and a bone with some meat on it. With that he strolled away from the house but he was in no great hurry.

"You'll get there soon enough," he thought to himself. "You now have the whole day before you and after that, with any luck, the moon will come up."

So he plodded on, just putting one foot in front of the other, stopping for a rest on the hills and having a good look round along the road. After a long, long way he came to the old woman lying by the roadside.

"You poor old woman," said Ash Lad. "You must be really hungry."

The old woman said yes, she was.

"Well then, I'll share what I have with you," said Ash Lad, and gave her the cheese rind.

"Are you cold too?" he asked her when he noticed that her teeth were chattering. "Here, you have my old jacket. It's not much good in the arms and the back is a bit worn but it was a good jacket when it was new."

"Just wait one moment," said the old woman and she dug down into her deep pocket. "Here is an old key," she said, "I have nothing better to give you, but when you look through the ring at the top you can see anything you wish to see."

When he arrived at the king's manor the cook was busy carrying water and this she was finding very hard work.

"That is much too heavy for you," said Ash Lad. "But it's just the sort of work I can do." The cook was delighted with this and in future she always let Ash Lad scrape out the porridge pot, but it was not long before he made many enemies because of this, and they told the king lies about him, saying that Ash Lad had claimed that he could do this or that.

So one day the king came to him and asked him if it was true that he could keep the fish safe in the pond so that the troll could not harm them. "That is what they tell me you have said," said the king.

"I have not said that," Ash Lad replied, "but if I had said it, I would certainly be able to do it."

The king told him that whether he had said it or not he would have to try if he wanted to keep the skin on his back. Ash Lad answered that he would now have to try since he had no wish to go about with red cuts under his jacket.

In the evening Ash Lad peeped through the key-ring and he saw that the troll was afraid of thyme, so he gathered all the thyme he could find and some he scattered on the water and some on dry land and the rest he scattered along the edges of the pond.

So the troll had to leave the fish in peace but the sheep had to suffer for it. The troll chased them over the crags and cliffs all night long.

Then one of the other servants began spreading tales saying that Ash Lad knew how to protect the sheep as well if only he chose to: yes, he had actually said that, it was true.

The king went to Ash Lad and told him just as he had done before – threatening to cut three broad red stripes from his back if he didn't do just what he had said.

In that case there was no help for it. Ash Lad thought it would be grand to wear the king's livery and a red jacket but he would rather do without them if he had to pay for these fine clothes with the skin off his back.

So he set about gathering thyme again but this task seemed never-ending because the sheep ate the thyme from each other's backs as soon as he had tied it to them. This went on and on for the sheep ate faster than he could manage to tie the thyme on them. In the end he made an ointment from thyme and tar and rubbed it on to them and then they stopped eating it. Next he gave the cattle and the horses the same thyme ointment treatment and so the troll left them all in peace.

One day the king was out hunting and he lost his way in the forest. He rode round and round for many days and had nothing to eat or drink and his clothes were so torn to pieces in the deep forest that in the end he had scarcely a rag to his back. Then the troll appeared and wanted to come to an agreement: if the troll could have the first thing the king met when he reached his own kingdom he would let him go home to his manor. The king was willing to agree to this for he felt sure that the first thing to meet him would be his little dog which always came fussing and scampering. But when he was approaching the manor-house, near enough to be seen, out came the king's eldest daughter to meet him, followed by all the people of the court. She welcomed him warmly but when he realised that she was the first to meet him he suddenly collapsed to the ground and since then he has been almost like a halfwit.

In the evening the troll was to come and fetch the princess. She wore her fine clothes and sat in a meadow by the tarn weeping and sobbing. A man called Colfox was supposed to accompany her but he was so scared that he climbed up into a tall fir tree and just stayed there. At that moment up came Ash Lad and sat down on the ground beside the princess and she was so glad to know that there were still Christian folk who were not afraid to be by her side.

"Lay your head on my lap," she said, "and I'll comb your hair."

Espen Ash Lad did as she asked and he fell asleep while she combed his hair. She took a gold ring from her finger and tied it tightly into his hair.

Just then the troll came along breathing noisily and so heavy-footed that the forest creaked and crashed for a mile round. When the troll saw Colfox sitting in the top of the fir tree like a little black cock he spat at him: "Pss!" he spat and both Colfox and the tall fir tree toppled to the ground, and there he lay floundering about like a fish out of water.

"Ho ho!" said the troll to the princess, "so you are sitting there combing a Christian man's hair and for that I shall eat you up."

"Phooey!" exclaimed Ash Lad who woke up at that moment and he peered at the troll through the key-ring.

"Hey, hey! What are staring at me for, eh?" the troll said and he hurled his iron stake at Ash Lad but he was so quick on his feet that he dodged on one side just as the troll hurled the stake which sank fifteen metres into the rock.

"Ha! What a feeble old woman's performance!" said Ash Lad. "Give me your toothpick and I'll show you how to throw!"

So the troll tugged out the stake in one pull and it was as long as three gate-posts on end. Meanwhile Ash Lad was staring up at the heavens in all directions.

"Hey! What are you staring at now?" the troll asked.

"I'm looking for the right star to throw it to," said Ash Lad. "Can you see that tiny little one in the north? That's the one."

"No, no," said the troll, "let's forget it. You mustn't throw away my iron stake."

"Very well," said Ash Lad. "You might as well have it back then. Perhaps you would prefer it if I threw it for a trip up to the moon?" No, the troll didn't like that idea either.

"Well then, how about Blind Man's Buff? Wouldn't you like to play Blind Man's Buff?" Ash Lad asked.

Yes, the troll thought that could be fun. "But you ought to have the blindfold first," said the troll.

"That's fine by me," said Ash Lad, "but it would be better if we drew lots, then we won't argue about it."

So, that's what was agreed. But Ash Lad arranged it so that

the troll was the first to have the blindfold over his eyes.

But you have never seen a game of Blind Man's Buff quite like this! They chased in and out of the trees and the troll stumbled and crashed into the trees so that the splinters flew and the wood creaked.

"Hey, hey!" the troll shrieked in a great rage. "How much longer does the troll have to be blind man?"

"Wait a bit longer," said Ash Lad, "and I'll stand still and call until you catch me."

Meanwhile he took a flax comb* and ran round to the other side of the tarn which was so deep that it had no bottom.

"Come on now," Ash Lad called, "I'm standing over here."

"I expect there are logs and trees in the way," said the troll.

"You should be able to hear that there are no trees here," said Ash Lad, and he swore that there were neither logs nor trees. "Just come over here."

So the game began again. Splash! And the troll fell into the tarn. Ash Lad hacked at his eyes with the spikes on the flax comb whenever he got his head above water.

The troll now asked so pathetically for his life that the lad took pity on him; but first of all he had to give up the princess and to bring back the other one whom he had stolen earlier, and he also had to promise to leave people and animals in peace. Then the troll was set free and he crept back to his home in the mountain.

Now Colfox became a brave man again. He came down from the fir tree, took the princess with him back to the manor-house and forced her to say that he was the one who had set her free. He then slunk down to take charge of the other

---

* A flax comb or heckling comb was used to separate and clean the tangled fibres of the raw flax before it could be spun and woven to make linen. The comb consisted of long sharp iron or brass nails set in a wooden block.

Ash Lad and the troll play Blind Man's Buff by Theodor Kittelsen.
Illustration © O. Væring Eftf. AS.

princess as well, even though Ash Lad had accompanied her as far as the garden. There was such joy in the manor that it was talked about throughout the country and the kingdom; and Colfox was to be married to the king's youngest daughter.

It seemed as if everything was going well but then everything was not well for the troll had gone down into the earth and stopped up all the springs of water. The troll thought to himself: "If I can't do any other mischief I'll see that they don't have any water for the wedding feast."

There was nothing to be done except to send for Ash Lad again. He found an iron stake fifteen metres long and six smiths to make it red hot. He then peeped through his keyring and saw where the troll was – just as clearly underground as above it – and he drove the stake down into the ground and into the troll's backbone and there was a smell of burnt flesh for miles around.

"Hey, hey!" shrieked the troll. "Get me out of here!" In no time at all he came storming out of the hole and he was singed right up to his neck. Ash Lad was not slow to act: he took hold of the troll and laid him out on a stake which had thyme tied round it and there he had to stay until he revealed where he had obtained new eyes to replace the eyes that Ash Lad had hacked out with the flax comb.

Eventually the troll said: "I stole a turnip and smeared it well with grease. Then I cut it to the sizes I needed and fixed them in with small nails, and better eyes I could not wish any Christian man to have."

Then the king came on the scene with the two princesses and wanted to see the troll. Colfox was also there bowing and scraping, like a fox on the trail with its nose to the ground and its tail in the air.

Suddenly the king caught sight of something glittering in Ash Lad's hair.

"What is that you have there?" he asked.

"Oh!" said Ash Lad. "That's the ring your daughter gave me when I rescued her from the troll."

And now it all came out exactly what had really happened. Colfox wept and pleaded for himself but no matter what he said there was no help for it – down he had to go into the snake pit and that was the end of him.

They then killed the troll, and after that they began to make merry and to drink and dance at Ash Lad's wedding, for now it was he who was the hero of the hour and so he won the youngest princess and half the kingdom.

And so I put my tale upon a sledge
To send to you whose wit has keener edge
But if you find your wit is not so fine
Then shame on you for finding fault with mine

Espen Ash Lad and the Good Helpers

Once upon a time there was a king and he had heard of a ship that could go as fast on land as it could on water. Such a ship he too wished to have. He promised that anyone who could build it would have his daughter for his wife and half the kingdom, and this he proclaimed in every church throughout the land. There were many who tried, for half the kingdom would be good to have, and the king's daughter would be worth having too. But things went badly for all those who tried.

Now there were three brothers who lived away in the woods. The eldest was called Peter, the middle one was Paul and the youngest was called Espen Ash Lad because he always sat poking and raking among the ashes. But on the Sunday when the proclamation was made about the ship the king wanted, by chance Ash Lad himself was at church and when he came home he told the others about it. Peter, who was the eldest, asked his mother for a pack of food for he wanted to set out at once to see if he could build the ship and win the king's daughter and half the kingdom.

So when he had settled the knapsack of food on his back, off he went. On the way he met a bent and pitiful old man.

"Where are you off to?" said the man.

"I'm going to the wood to make a food bowl for my father," said Peter. "He doesn't like to eat with the rest of us."

"Let it be a bowl then!" said the man. "What have you got in your knapsack?"

"Manure," said Peter.

"Let it be manure then!" said the old man.

So Peter strode off into the oak wood and chopped and built as well as he could, but however much he chopped and built, the result was just one bowl after another. As the day wore on he decided to have something to eat and he opened his knapsack, but it wasn't food he found there. Since he now had nothing to eat and his carpentry was not going any better, he was tired of working so he put the axe and the knapsack on his back and went home to his parents again.

Then Paul wanted to go and try his luck to see if he could build the ship and win the king's daughter and half the kingdom. He asked his mother for some food to take and when she gave it to him he put the knapsack on his back and set off for the woods. On the way he met an old man who was bent and pitiful.

"Where are you off to?" asked the man

"Oh, I'm going to the wood to make a pig-trough for our little piglet," said Paul.

"Let it be a pig-trough then!" said the man. "What have you got in your knapsack?"

"Manure," said Paul.

"Let it be manure then!" said the man.

So Paul strode off into the wood and chopped and built as well as he could, but however much he cut and shaped the wood the result was nothing but pig-troughs and more pig-troughs. He didn't give up though but worked on until late into the afternoon before he thought about having something to eat. Then all at once he suddenly felt so hungry that he just had to take up his knapsack. But there was no food in it! Paul was so angry that he turned the sack inside out and threw it against a tree-stump. Then he picked up his axe and marched out of the wood and went straight home.

When Paul returned home Espen Ash Lad wanted to set off
and he asked his mother for some food to take.

"Perhaps I'll be able to build the ship and win the king's
daughter and half the kingdom," he said.

"Oh yes! That's very likely," said his mother. "You, who
never do anything except poke about and rake among the
ashes! No, you'll not get any food to take."

Ash Lad didn't give up even so. He pleaded for so long that
in the end he was allowed to go. He didn't get any food but he
managed to sneak a couple of oatcakes and a drop of flat ale,
and went on his way.

When he had walked for a while he met the same bent,
scruffy, pitiful old man.

"Where are you off to?" asked the man

"Oh, I'm going into the woods, and if all goes well, I'll
build a ship that will go as fast on land as it does on the water,"
said Ash Lad. "The king has promised that the one who can
build such a ship will have the king's daughter and half the
kingdom."

"What have you got in your sack?" the man asked.

"Oh, nothing much to speak of. It should really be a pack
of food," Ash Lad replied.

"If you would give me just a little of what you have," said
the man, "I'll be able to help you."

"I'll do that willingly," said Espen Ash Lad, "but it's nothing more than two oat cakes and a drop of stale ale."

It was all the same to him whatever it was; if only he got it,
he would certainly help him.

When they came to an old oak tree in the wood the man
said, "Now you must cut out a chip and then put it in again
exactly where it came from. And when you have done that you
can lie down and go to sleep."

Well, Ash Lad did just as he had been told. He lay down to

sleep and in his sleep he seemed to hear chopping and hammering and carpentry, sawing and joinery, but he was unable to wake up before the man woke him. And then, there stood the ship by the oak tree, all completed.

"Now," said the old greybeard, "you have to climb on board and you must take with you everyone you meet."

Espen Ash Lad thanked him for the ship, said he would do just as the man had told him, and sailed away.

When he had sailed for a while he came across a tall, scrawny fellow lying on a hillside and eating rubble.

"What sort of a fellow are you, lying there eating rubble?" asked Ash Lad, and the scrawny one replied that he was so hungry for meat that he could never have enough and so he had to eat rubble. He then asked if he could come along in the ship.

"Yes," said Ash Lad. "If you want to come along just climb on board." Yes, he would like to do that; and he took some big rocks with him for food.

When they had sailed further on they came across a fellow lying on a sunny hillside sucking on the tap of an ale cask.

"What sort of a fellow are you?" asked Espen Ash Lad, "and why are you lying there sucking on an ale tap?"

"Well," said the man, "when you don't have the barrel, you have to be thankful for the tap. I've such a thirst that I can never get enough ale and wine." He then asked if he could come along with them on board the ship.

"If you want to come," said Ash Lad, "Just climb on board." Yes, he would like to do that. He climbed on board taking with him the ale-tap for the sake of his thirst.

When they had sailed a little further they came across a man lying with one ear to the ground listening.

"What sort of a fellow are you?" asked Espen Ash Lad, "and why are you lying on the ground listening?"

"I'm listening to the grass," he said. "You see, I have such good hearing that I can hear it growing." Then he asked if he could come with them on the ship and there was no question of saying, "No."

"If you want to come," said Ash Lad, "just climb on board." Yes, he would like to come, so he too climbed on board.

When they had sailed a little further they came across a man who stood just aiming a gun.

"What sort of a fellow are you?" said Ash Lad. "And what's the good of standing just aiming like that?"

"I have such keen eyesight," said the man, "that I can easily shoot straight to the world's end."

Then he asked if he could come with them on the ship.

"If you want to come," said Ash Lad, "Just climb on board." Yes, he would like to come, so he too climbed on board.

When they had sailed a little further they came across a man who was hopping round on one leg, and on the other leg he had seven weights.

"What sort of a fellow are you?" Ash Lad asked. "And what's the point of hopping about on one leg and having seven weights on the other?"

"I so easily fly off into the air," said the man, "that if I walked on both feet I would come to the end of the world in less than five minutes."

Then he asked if he could come with them on the ship.

"If you want to come," said Ash Lad, "just climb on board." Yes, he would like to come, so he climbed on board to join Ash Lad and his fellow travellers.

When they had sailed a little further they came across a man who stood holding his hand over his mouth.

"What sort of a fellow are you?" asked Ash Lad. "And

Man flying through the air by Theodor Kittelsen.
Illustration © O. Væring Eftf. AS.

why are you standing there like that holding your hand in front of your mouth?"

"Oh," he said, "I've got seven summers and fifteen winters inside my body so I had better hold my hand before my mouth because if I let them all out that would put an end to the world straight away." Then he asked if he could come with them.

"If you want come," said Ash Lad, "just climb on board."

Yes, he would like to come, so he climbed on board the ship to join the others.

When they had sailed for quite some distance they arrived at the king's manor-house. Ash Lad strode straight to the king and said that the ship was standing ready out in the courtyard and he now wished to have the king's daughter just as the king had promised.

The king was not too pleased with this for Ash Lad did not appear at all presentable. He was dirty and scruffy and the king had not the slightest wish to give his daughter to such a tramp. He said he would have to wait a while. He could not have the princess before he had emptied a meat storehouse which contained three hundred barrels of meat belonging to the king. The king said, "If you can get it done by tomorrow morning then you shall have her."

"I shall try," said Ash Lad, "but may I ask for permission to take one of my friends with me?"

Yes, he could do that, said the king. He could take all six if he wanted to. For the king thought he wouldn't be able to do it even if he had six hundred to help him.

Ash Lad took with him only the man who ate rubble and was always so hungry for meat. When they had opened up the storehouse he ate up everything except six small salted hams, just one for each of the others. So Ash Lad went to the king and told him that the storehouse was now empty, so now he could surely have the king's daughter.

The king went out to the storehouse and saw that it was indeed quite empty, but Ash Lad was still dirty and scruffy and the king thought it was really unseemly for such a ragamuffin to have his daughter. So he said he had a cellar full of ale and old wine, three hundred casks of each, which he wanted to have drunk up before he could give permission. "If you can drink it all up by this time tomorrow, then you shall have her."

"I shall try," said Ash Lad, "but may I take one of my friends with me?"

"Yes, of course," said the king. He thought he had so much ale and wine that there was more than enough for all seven of them.

Ash Lad took with him the man who sucked on the ale-tap and was always so thirsty for ale. Then the king locked them in the cellar. The man drank barrel after barrel as long as there was anything left, but he saved a little from the last barrel so that his companions should have a drop as well.

In the morning the cellar was unlocked and Ash Lad went straight to the king and said he had finished up the ale and wine, so now he would surely have the king's daughter just as he had been promised.

"Well," said the king, "first of all I must go down to the cellar and see for myself," for he didn't believe him. When he came down to the cellar he saw that all the barrels were empty. But Ash Lad was still dirty and scruffy and the king didn't think much of having him as a son-in-law. So he said that if he could fetch water from the end of the world in ten minutes for the princess's tea, then he should have both the princess and half the kingdom. For he thought that was totally impossible.

"I'll have to try then," said Ash Lad.

So, he found the man who hobbled about on one leg and had seven weights on the other and told him to take off the weights and use both of his legs to go as fast as he could, for he had to fetch water from the end of the world in ten minutes for the princess's tea.

He took off the weights, took hold of a pail, set off and was gone in the wink of an eye. But time went by, dragging endlessly, and still he didn't come back. In the end there were only three minutes left before time ran out, and the king was as delighted as if he had been given a fortune.

But then Ash Lad called to the man who listened to the grass growing and told him to listen to find out where the other fellow had got to.

"He's fallen asleep by the well," he said. "I can hear him snoring and the troll is combing his hair."

So Ash Lad shouted to the man who could shoot straight to the end of the world to put a bullet into the troll. This he did! He shot the troll right in the eye. Then the troll let out such a roar that the man who was supposed to be fetching the water for the tea woke up. And when he reached the king's manorhouse there was still one minute left.

Ash Lad strode in to the king and said that here was the water, and now he would certainly have the king's daughter. There was no more to be said.

But the king thought Ash Lad was still as dirty and scruffy as ever and he would not have him for a son-in-law. So he said he had one thousand cubic metres of wood which he was going to use in the bath-house to dry the corn. "If you can manage to sit in there and burn it up, then you shall have her – there's no question about that."

"I shall try," said Ash Lad, "but may I have permission to take one of my companions with me?"

"Yes," said the king, "you can take all six if you like." For he thought it would be quite hot enough for all of them.

Ash Lad took with him the man who had fifteen winters and seven summers in his body and in the evening they went into the bath-house. But the king had made it very hot; there was a fire so big and hot that they could easily have made cast-iron stoves in it. They could not get out for no sooner were they inside than the king barred the door and added a couple of extra padlocks.

Ash Lad said to the man, "You will have to release six or seven winters until it is a reasonable summer warmth in here."

Then they were able to hold out in there but during the night it became quite chilly so Ash Lad said he must warm it up with a couple of summers. When that had been done they slept well into the next day. But when they heard the king pottering about outside Ash Lad said, "Now you must let out a couple of winters but send the last one right into his face."

So he did just that and when the king unlocked the bath-house door expecting to see them lying there burnt to death, there they sat shivering and freezing so that their teeth rattled. The man with the fifteen winters in his body let out the last one straight into the king's eyes so that he had a big chilblain on his face.

"Now do I get the princess?" said Ash Lad.

"Yes! Take her and keep her and have the kingdom as well!" said the king, for he did not dare to say "No" any longer.

So they held the wedding and celebrated and made merry and fired shots to scare away the troll-witches.

While they were running about scrabbling for a bullet wadding they mistook me for one and gave me some porridge in a flask and some milk in a basket and then shot me straight here so that I could tell you how it all happened.

Ash Lad and the King's Hares

Once upon a time there was a poor farmer who had to give up his farm to his landlord. However, he still had his three sons whose names were Peter, Paul and Espen Ash Lad. They lived at home and had such an easy life that they were unwilling to lend a hand to anything. They thought they were superior to anything else and that nothing was too good for them.

One day Peter heard that the king wanted a herdsman to look after his hares. He told his father that to keep watch over the king's hares would suit him fine, for then he would not be serving any man lower than the king himself, so he said he would go. But his father believed that there might be work for which he was better suited, for whoever had to keep guard over the hares would have to be energetic and light on his feet and no lazy-bones. When the hares were rushing about in all directions he would have to dance to a very different tune than just pottering about from room to room at home.

But it was all to no purpose. Peter was determined to go to see the king, so he put his knapsack on his back and strode off down the hill. When he had walked a very long way – further than far – he came across an old woman with her nose stuck fast in a log of wood. He watched her as she tugged and struggled to get free and he burst into loud laughter.

"Don't stand there sniggering," said the old woman, "come and help an old body. I was just chopping up some firewood but I got my nose stuck fast in here, and now I have stood

*The old woman whose nose was stuck in a log by Erik
Werenskiold. Illustration © O. Væring Eftf. AS.*

pulling and struggling and had nothing to eat for a hundred years." At this Peter laughed more and more. He thought it was all so funny and told her that if she had stood like that for a hundred years she could easily hold out for another hundred years.

When he arrived at the king's manor he was made herdsman on the spot. It was not a hard life working there. He would have good food and good wages – and perhaps the king's daughter's hand in marriage as well. But if just one of the king's hares was lost they would cut three red stripes from his back and throw him into a snake pit.

Peter thought it would be a simple task to keep watch on these hares for they seemed as tame as a flock of sheep, and just so long as they kept to the fields where the cattle grazed he managed to keep all the hares together in one flock. But as the day wore on and the sun began to burn, the hares went into the wood where they began to scatter and scuttle off in all directions. Peter ran after them and chased them as hard as he could as long as there was any chance of catching up with even one of them. In the end he couldn't find a single hare, and by then he was almost gasping for breath with all the effort. After that he saw nothing more of them.

Towards evening he sauntered on the way home and stood by the gate and called to them, but no hares came. When he reached the king's manor there stood the king all ready with his knife. He cut three red strips out of his back, rubbed salt and pepper into the wounds and then threw him into the snake pit.

Some time later Paul decided that he too would like to go and be herdsman to the king's hares. His father gave him the same warning as he had given Peter but Paul was determined to set off and nothing was going to stop him. But things went neither better nor worse for him than they had for Peter. The old woman still stood pulling and struggling to free her nose from the log; Paul laughed and thought it was just as funny, and left her standing there tugging away. He got the job of herdsman at once without any question. But the hares ran from him and away all over the hills and he dashed about until he panted like a sheep dog in the heat of the sun. When he returned to the king's manor in the evening without the hares the king stood in the courtyard ready with his knife.

He cut three red stripes out of this back, rubbed salt and pepper in the wounds and down he went into the snake pit.

Some time later Espen Ash Lad told his father that now he was keen to set off and be herdsman to the king's hares. Ash Lad thought it would be just the right sort of work for him – to wander through the fields and woods where the strawberries grew, rambling after a flock of hares and lying dozing and taking life easily on the sunny hillsides. His father's opinion was that there was surely work that would be more suitable for him, but if things didn't go worse for Ash Lad than they had gone for his brothers they were unlikely to go any better.

The man who wanted to guard the king's hares could not dawdle about like a lazybones with lead weights in his shoes or like a fly on a tar brush; and when the hares begin to leap and skip around in all directions and all over the hills it is not even as easy as catching fleas with gloves on. The man who could do that work and escape with his back intact had to be quicker than quick and to fly about faster than a dried skin or a bird's wing flies in the wind.

"Well, that can't be helped," said Ash Lad. He would go to the king's manor and work for the king, for he would not work for any lesser man. The hares he would surely keep under control; they couldn't be more difficult than goats or calves. So Ash Lad put his knapsack on his back and strolled off down the hill.

When he had gone a very long way – further than far – and

he began to feel really hungry, he came to the old woman standing with her nose in the log tugging and struggling trying to get free.

"Good day, grandmother," said Ash Lad. "Are you standing there sharpening your nose, you poor old lady?"

"Well now!" said the old woman, "nobody has called me 'mother' for a hundred years. Please come and help me get free and give me a little something to eat. I have not had any food in my mouth for all those years. Then I will do you a good turn too."

Yes, Ash Lad thought, she certainly is in need of something to eat and drink. So he split the log for her so that she could get her nose out and, with that done, he sat down to share his food with her. The old woman had a good appetite and ate up most of the food-pack.

When they had finished their meal she gave Ash Lad a pipe, like a little flute, which was made so that when he blew into one end of it, everything he wanted to get rid of was scattered to the corners of the earth; and when he blew into the other end everything came back again; and if the pipe was lost or taken from him he just had to wish he had it back and it would return to him.

"That is quite a pipe!" said Ash Lad.

When he came to the king's manor they made him hare herdsman straight away. Working there was no great hardship. He would have food and wages and, if he was able to keep the king's hares so that none of them were lost, he might have the king's daughter too. But, if any of them got away, even if it was only a young one, they would cut three red stripes from his back. The king was so sure that Espen Ash Lad would not succeed in this that he began to sharpen his knife on the spot.

It should be no great task to keep watch on these hares, thought Ash Lad, for they seemed almost as tame as a flock of sheep; and as long as they kept to where the cattle grazed and in the fields near the manor house he kept them altogether in one flock. But as the day wore on, when they went up on to the wooded hillside and the sun began to shine hot on the slopes, then the hares began to scatter all over the hills.

"Hey! Hey!" Ash Lad yelled, "are you all going?" He blew into one end of the pipe and they ran off in all directions and every one disappeared. Ash Lad went on and came to a pit-stead where they burned charcoal in the old days and there he blew into the other end of the pipe and, almost before he realised it, there were all the hares all lined up in rows just like soldiers on parade.

"This is quite a pipe, this is," said Ash Lad to himself and he lay down to sleep on a sunny hill slope. The hares ran around and looked after themselves until evening. Then he piped them all together again and brought them down to the king's manor like a flock of sheep.

The king, the queen and the princess stood on the balcony and wondered what sort of fellow this was who managed to guard the hares so well and bring them all home again. The king counted them again and again, and then counted them again on his fingers, but not even one young hare was missing.

"That's a lad to wonder at," said the princess.

The following day Espen Ash Lad went off to the woods again to keep watch on the hares. But when he was lying down for a rest in the strawberry fields, they sent the housemaid from the manor to find out how he managed to guard the king's hares so well. So Ash Lad took out his pipe and showed it to her and blew into one end and the hares scattered like the wind, away over all the crests of the hills. Then he blew into the other end and they all came scampering back and lined up in rows again.

"What a wonderful pipe that is!" said the maid. She would willingly give him a hundred dollars for it if he would sell it.

"Yes," agreed Ash Lad, "it is a wonderful pipe but it is not for sale for cash." However, if she would give him the hundred dollars and a kiss for each dollar then she could have it.

Yes, she would happily give him two kisses for every dollar and say, "Thank you" as well. So she got the pipe.

But when she returned to the king's manor the pipe had disappeared; for Ash Lad had made a wish to get it back. So in the evening he came home with the hares just like any other flock of sheep, and however often the king counted them he had to accept that not a single hare was missing.

On the third day when Ash Lad was keeping watch over the hares they sent the princess to try to get the pipe from him. She appeared as happy as a lark and offered him two hundred dollars if he would sell her the pipe and tell her how to take it home safely.

"Yes," said Ash Lad. "It is a very special pipe, but it is not for sale." However, for her, he might sell it. If she would give him two hundred dollars and a kiss for every dollar as well, then she could have the pipe. If she wished to keep it she would have to keep a close eye on it: that was her problem.

The princess thought this was a high price to pay for a hare-pipe and she was not happy about giving him all those kisses. But since they were in the wood no-one could see or hear anything – so there was no help for it, for she really must have the pipe.

So, when Ash Lad had had all the kisses he was entitled to, she got the pipe. She clutched it close to her and held on to it tightly all the way but when she arrived at the king's manor and was about to show it, it had slipped through her fingers and disappeared.

On the next day the queen herself decided to go and get the

pipe from him. She intended to make sure that she would bring it home safely. She was quite stingy with her money and wouldn't offer more than fifty dollars but in the end she had to raise this to three hundred. Ash Lad said this was a quite ridiculous price for such a very special pipe but since it was for her he might consider it if she gave him three hundred dollars and a hearty kiss for every dollar as well. She was very happy to agree and gave him the kisses generously and willingly.

When she had hold of the pipe she tied it fast to herself and hid it away securely but things went no better for her than for the others, for when she was going to bring it out to show the king, it had disappeared.

And in the evening Espen Ash lad came driving the king's hares like a flock of tame sheep.

"This is all stuff and nonsense," said the king. "It seems I shall have to go myself if we are to get this wretched pipe from him. There seems to be no other way."

When on the following day Ash Lad was well into the woods with the hares, the king went looking for him and found him lying on the same sunny hillside where the women had had their encounter with him.

Ash Lad and the king got on well with each other and he showed him the pipe and blew first on one end and then on the other. The king thought it was a wonderful pipe and he would definitely like to buy it even if he had to give a thousand dollars for it.

"Yes," said Ash Lad. "It is a very special pipe but it is not for sale for cash. But can you see that white mare down there in the marshland behind that big spruce tree?" and he pointed into the wood.

"Yes, of course," said the king. "That is my own horse, Kvita. I recognise her easily enough."

"Well," said Ash Lad. "If you will give me a thousand dollars and go and kiss Kvita, then you shall have my pipe.

"Isn't it for sale for any other price?" the king asked.

"No, it is not," said Espen Ash Lad.

"I see," said the king, "but may I be permitted to put my silk handkerchief between myself and the horse?"

Yes, he could do that. So he got the pipe and he put it in his purse and the purse he put in his pocket and then buttoned up the pocket-flap tightly. He then set off for home and was all set to pull out the pipe but he was no better off than the women folk: he didn't have the pipe any more than they had. And Ash Lad came home driving the flock of hares – and not a single one was missing.

The king was annoyed and angry because Ash Lad had tricked them all and cheated him, especially, out of the pipe. Now, he said, Ash Lad must lose his life – there was no question of that. The queen agreed with this – it was best that such a scoundrel should be severely punished.

Espen Ash Lad thought this was neither right nor fair for he had done nothing but what they had told him to do. He had merely protected his back and his life as best he could.

That was how things stood, said the king: but if he could fill the great brewing vat so full with lies that it overflowed, then he might keep his life.

Ash Lad thought that would not be either a long or difficult task; he was quite sure he could do that successfully. So he began to tell all that had happened from the beginning. He told the story of the old woman with her nose stuck fast in the log of wood; and then suddenly he said: "I shall have to tell lies now if the vat is ever to be full."

So he told the story of the pipe and of the housemaid who came and wanted to buy it for a hundred dollars and of all the kisses she had to give him as well, as they lay on the hillside

Ash Lad kisses the Queen by Erik Werenskiold. Illustration © O. Væring Eftf. AS.

in the wood. And then he told how the princess had kissed him in exchange for the pipe because no-one could see or hear them hidden in the wood.

"I shall really have to lie some more," said Espen Ash Lad, "if the vat is to be filled."

So he told of the queen's visit and how mean she was about money but how generous she had been with her smacking kisses.

"Now, I shall have to lie really well if the vat is ever to be full," said Espen Ash Lad.

"Personally," said the king, "I think it is full enough already."

"Oh no, it isn't," said the queen.

So Ash Lad began to tell how the king came to see him and about the white horse down in the marshes – and how, if the king really wished to have the pipe, then he must – he must – "forgive me, but I must continue to make up lies if the vat is ever to be full," said Espen Ash Lad.

"Stop! Stop! Lad. It's full to the brim," roared the king. "Can't you see that it's overflowing!"

So both the king and the queen considered it by far the best that he should have the princess and half the kingdom. There was nothing else to be done.

"That was quite a pipe," said Espen Ash Lad.

Soria Moria Castle

Once upon a time there was a man and his wife who had a son whose name was Halvor. Right from the time when he was a small boy he had been unwilling to do anything. He just sat and poked among the ashes all day long. His parents sent him away to learn many different trades but Halvor would not stay anywhere long. When he had been away for a few days he ran away back home and just sat on the hearth and raked among the ashes as before. But one day a skipper arrived and asked him if he would like to go to sea with him and see foreign lands. Yes, indeed, that he would like to do – and he was ready in the twinkling of an eye.

After they had been sailing a long time a great storm blew up and when it was over and all was calm again they had no idea where they were. They had been driven on to a strange coast which none of them knew anything about. Since the air was so still that not even a feather stirred and they lay becalmed, Halvor asked the skipper if he could go ashore and look round for he would rather go for a walk than just lie about and sleep.

The skipper said "Do you think you are in a fit state to show yourself to people? You don't have any other clothes than those rags you stand there and go about in."

Halvor insisted and eventually he was given permission to go but on condition that he had to return as soon as the wind blew up again. So off he went and he discovered a beautiful land. Everywhere there were great plains with cultivated fields and pastures but he did not see any sign at all of people. Then the wind began to blow but Halvor didn't think he had seen enough yet. He wanted to walk on a little longer to see if he could find any people. After a while he came to a wide road which was so level that you could roll an egg along it. Halvor followed this road and towards evening he saw, in the far distance, a great castle shining in the bright light. He had now been walking the whole day and had almost nothing to eat so now he was really hungry, but the nearer he came to the castle the more afraid he became.

Inside the castle Halvor went into the kitchen where there was a fire burning. It was the finest kitchen he had ever set eyes on with pans and saucepans of gold and silver. But there was not a sign of any people. When Halvor had stood there a while and no-one appeared he went over and opened a door and inside sat a princess with a spinning wheel.

"Oh no! Oh no!" she cried. "What Christian folk dare to venture here? You had better go away again, otherwise the troll will gobble you up, for a troll with three heads lives here."

"It would be all the same to me if it had four heads," said Halvor, "I should still want to see it. And I am not going away because I have done nothing wrong. But you must give me something to eat; I am really very hungry."

When Halvor had eaten his fill, the princess told him to try to wield the sword which hung on the wall, but he couldn't manage it. He couldn't even lift it.

"Well then," said the princess, "you must take a swig from the flask that hangs beside it. That is what the troll does whenever it goes out to use the sword."

Halvor took a swig and straight away he was able to wield the sword as if it weighed nothing at all.

"Now," he thought, "just let the troll come." And just at

that moment the troll came blustering in; and Halvor hid himself behind the door.

"Phew! It smells of Christian blood in here," said the troll and thrust his head through the doorway.

"Yes, it does," said Halvor, "and you will soon see why." And with that he cut off all the troll's heads.

The princess was so happy now that she had been freed and she danced and sang. But then she came to think of her sisters. "How I wish that my sisters were free as well!" she said.

"Where are they then?" Halvor asked.

She told him that one of them was taken away by a troll to a castle which was forty miles away and the other had been taken by another troll to a castle sixty miles beyond that. Then she pointed to the troll's body which lay there and said: "First you must help me get this corpse out of here."

That was no problem. Halvor was so strong that he had everything cleared away and cleaned up in no time at all. Then he spent a pleasant and relaxing day before setting off at dawn the next morning. He took no time to rest on the way but he walked and ran the whole day. When he caught sight of the castle he felt a little afraid again. It was much grander than the other castle but here too there was no-one to be seen. Halvor went into the kitchen and then further inside until he found the princess.

"Oh no!" she cried. "Does a Christian really dare to come here? I don't know how long it is since I came here but in all that time I have not set eyes on a Christian soul. But it would be best if you left again for a troll with six heads lives here."

"No!" said Halvor. "I won't leave, not even if he had six more heads."

"He will gobble you up alive," said the princess.

But that didn't worry Halvor who had no intention of going – he wasn't afraid of the troll. But he really would like something to eat and drink. He was hungry after his journey. So he was given as much as he wanted and then the princess again begged him to leave.

"No!" Halvor said. "I won't go for I have done nothing wrong and I have nothing to be afraid of."

"The troll won't be concerned with that," said the princess. "He will just grab hold of you without asking about rights or permission, but since you are determined not to go you had better try to wield the sword that the troll uses to fight with."

Halvor was unable to swing the sword so the princess said he must take a swig from the flask hanging beside it. When he had done this he was able to wield the sword easily.

And just at that moment the troll appeared. It was so big and burly that it had to turn sideways in order to get through the door. When the first head came through the troll roared, "Pooh! It smells of Christian blood in here." And without more ado Halvor cut off the first head and then all the others.

The princess was so happy that she couldn't keep still but then she remembered her sisters and wished that they too could be set free.

Halvor thought that could easily be arranged and he was eager to set off at once but first he had to help the princess to remove the troll's corpse. The next morning he was on his way once more.

It was a long way to the castle and he had to walk and run fast in order to get there in time. As twilight fell he caught sight of the castle and it was even grander than the other two. This time he was not in the least afraid and walked straight into the kitchen and then further inside; and there sat a princess who was more beautiful than any other.

Like the other princesses she told him that there hadn't been any Christian folk there since she had arrived and she too begged him to leave at once, otherwise the troll would eat him

Ash Lad beheads the troll by Erik Werenskiold.
Illustration © O. Væring Eftf. AS.

alive, and it had nine heads, she said.

Halvor replied that even if it had nine more heads he was still not going anywhere, and he settled himself down by the fire.

The princess begged him to leave as earnestly as she could but Halvor insisted that he would stay.

"Let the troll come whenever he likes," he said.

So she gave him the troll's sword and told him to take a swig from the flask so that he would be able to wield it. Just then the troll came rushing in like the wind. This one was even bigger and burlier than both the others and it also had to turn sideways in order to get through the doorway.

"Pooh!" said the troll. "It smells of the blood of a Christian man in here."

Without more ado Halvor cut off the first head and then all the others, but the last one was the toughest of them all. To get that one off was the hardest task Halvor had ever had to do, although he knew he had the strength to do it.

At last all the princesses were together at the castle and they were happier than they had ever been. They were fond of Halvor and he was fond of them. He could choose the one he liked best for his bride. The youngest princess was the one who was fondest of him. But after a while Halvor became downcast and moody. The princesses asked him if he didn't like their company and if there was something that he missed. Oh, he was very content to be with them and they had enough of everything, and he had a good life in every way, but he longed for his home and his parents whom he would so much like to see again. The princesses were sure that could be arranged.

They told him, "You can go and return without any harm coming to you if only you do as we tell you."

Yes, he would do exactly as they said. So they dressed him

as if he were the grandest prince and put a ring on his finger with which he could wish himself there and back again; but they said he must never take it off and he must never mention them, otherwise all their happiness would come to an end and he would never see them again.

"If only I was at home and home was here!" said Halvor; and immediately his wish came true. Before he knew it, he was standing outside his parents' cottage.

It was dusk and when they saw such a finely dressed stranger had arrived they were quite bewildered and bowed and curtsied. Halvor asked if he could spend the night there.

No, indeed he could not. We don't have this and we don't have that or anything that such a lord would expect. His parents told him it would be far better if he went up to the farmhouse, saying it is not very far – you can see the chimney-tops from here – and there they have plenty of everything.

Halvor had no wish to do that; he wished to stay with them. But they insisted that he should go up to the farmhouse because there he was sure to get food and drink, while they didn't even have a chair to offer him.

"No," said Halvor. "I'll not go up there until early tomorrow morning. Let me stay here tonight. I can easily sit on the hearth."

They couldn't refuse him that and so Halvor sat on the hearth and began to rake among the ashes just as he used to do when he lived at home and lounged about there.

They talked about many things and they told Halvor about this and that, and eventually Halvor asked them if they had ever had any children.

Yes, they had had a son called Halvor, but they had no idea what had become of him and they didn't know whether he was alive or dead.

"Couldn't that son be me, perhaps?" said Halvor.

"Oh, I would know him well enough," said the old woman getting up. "Halvor was so lazy and idle that he would never do the slightest thing; and his clothes were always in rags and tatters. He could never have become such a fine gentleman as you."

Soon afterwards the old woman went over to the fireplace to poke up the fire and when the glow from the blaze shone on Halvor's face just as it did when he lived at home and raked about in the ashes, she recognised him at once.

"Well, Bless me!" she cried. "Is it really you, Halvor?" There was such happiness for the old parents; they were overjoyed. Halvor had to tell them everything that had happened to him, and his mother was so proud of him that she wanted to take him up to the big farmhouse straight away to show him to the girls there who had always thought they were so superior.

She went first and Halvor came later. When she got there she told them that Halvor had come home again and now they would see how grand he was; he looks like a prince, she said.

"Of course, he does!" replied the girls and tossed their heads. "He's more likely to be the same ragamuffin he always was." And just at that moment in walked Halvor and the girls were so flustered because they had left their skirts by the hearth, where they had been sitting picking off fleas, and they had run out in just their petticoats. When they came back inside they were so ashamed that they hardly dared to look at Halvor to whom they had always been so haughty and scornful.

"Well now," said Halvor. "You have always considered yourselves to be so smart and beautiful and that no-one could be as grand as you, but you should see the eldest of the princesses I have set free. Compared with her you look no better than herdsmaids. And the next eldest princess is even more beautiful; but the youngest, who is my sweetheart, is more beautiful than the sun and the moon. If only they had been here, you could see for yourselves."

He had only just spoken these words when the princesses stood before them and he was horrified as he remembered what they had told him.

There were great celebrations at the farmhouse for the princesses but they would not stay. They said they wanted to go down to meet Halvor's parents and so they would go out and look around.

Halvor went with them and they came to a large lake near the farmhouse and close by the water there was a lovely green slope where the princesses said they would like to sit and rest for a while. They thought it was so pleasant to sit and look out over the water.

When they had sat a while the youngest princess said: "Let me comb your hair, shall I, Halvor?" Halvor was happy to agree to this and he laid his head in her lap while she combed his hair. It wasn't long before Halvor fell asleep and she took her ring off his finger and replaced it with another. Then she said to her sisters:

"Hold my hand and I'll hold yours – and let us wish that we were in Soria Moria Castle."

When Halvor woke up he realised that he had lost the princesses and he began to weep and wail. He was so upset that nothing could console him. However much his parents pleaded with him he would not stay at home with them. He said goodbye to them saying that he would probably never see them again, for if he didn't find the princesses he didn't think life would be worth living.

He still had three hundred dollars left so he put them in his pocket and went on his way. He had walked quite some distance when he met a man with a good-looking horse which he thought he would buy. So he began to bargain with the man who said "Well, I hadn't really thought of selling it but if we could reach some agreement, then perhaps..."

Halvor asked how much he wanted for it.

"I didn't give much for it," the man said, "and it isn't worth much either. It's a good enough horse to ride but it's not much use for hauling anything. But it can carry you and your knapsack easily enough, if you are willing to walk now and then."

Eventually they agreed on the price and Halvor placed his knapsack up on the horse and then he sometimes walked and sometimes he rode. In the evening he came to a green meadow where a great tree stood and he decided to sit under it. He let the horse loose and unloaded his knapsack.

At daybreak he set off on his way again for he was unable to rest. He walked and he rode the whole day long through a great forest where there were many green glades which shone brightly through the trees. He didn't know where he was or where he was going but he only stopped to rest when his horse needed to graze. For himself, he opened his knapsack for a snack when he came to one of the green glades. He walked and he rode and he began to think he would never come to the end of the forest. But at dusk on the second day he saw a light shining through the trees.

"If only there were people about," Halvor thought. "I could warm myself and get something to eat."

When he came up to the light he saw that it came from a wretched little hut and through the window he saw an old couple. They were so old, and grey-haired like a pair of doves; and the old woman had a nose so long that as she sat by the hearth she used it to poke the fire.

"Good evening!" said Halvor.

"Good evening!" said the old woman. "What errand brings

Opposite, three princesses sitting by the lake by Erik Werenskiold. Illustration © O. Væring Eftf. AS.

you here? No Christian folk have been here for more than a hundred years."

Halvor said that he wished to go to Soria Moria Castle and asked her if she knew the way there.

"No," said the old woman, "but soon the moon will come up and I can ask him. He's sure to know because he shines on everything."

When the moon rose bright and clear over the tree-tops, the old woman went outside and shrieked:

"Oh moon! Oh moon! Can you tell me the way to Soria Moria Castle?"

"No, I can't," said the moon, "the last time I shone there a cloud was in the way."

"Wait a little," the old woman said to Halvor. "The west wind will soon be coming and he's sure to know for he puffs and blows in every corner."

When the old woman came inside again she said, "Well, well. I see you have a horse too. Let the poor animal loose in our paddock. Don't let it stand here by the door and go hungry. Would you like to do a swap with me for it? We have a pair of old boots here in which you can stride twenty miles with every step. You can have the boots in exchange for your horse and then you will get to Soria Moria Castle all the sooner."

Halvor was willing to agree to this at once and the old woman was so pleased to have the horse that she wanted to dance for joy. "Now I too can ride to church," she said.

Halvor was restless and anxious to be on his way but the old woman said there was no hurry. "Just lie down on the bench and get a little sleep," she said, "for we don't have a bed for you. I'll keep an eye open for the west wind when he comes."

Suddenly, out of the blue, the west wind came roaring,

whistling and groaning in the walls. The old woman ran out-side: "West wind! West wind! Can you tell me the way to Soria Moria Castle? There's someone here who wants to go there."

"Yes," said the west wind. "I know it very well. I'm just on my way there now to dry some clothes for the wedding which is going to take place. If he is quick on his feet he can come with me."

Halvor rushed out at once.

"You'll have to be quick if you want to keep up with me," said the west wind as he set off over heath and hill and over mountain and moorland, and Halvor had a struggle to keep up.

The west wind said, "Now, I don't have the time to stay with you any longer. I have to go and blow down a plantation of spruce trees before I go on to the drying-ground to dry the clothes. But if you go along the side of the hill you will come to some girls washing clothes, and from there you haven't far to go to Soria Moria Castle.

Some time later Halvor reached the girls who were wash-ing clothes and they asked him if he had seen anything of the west wind who was supposed to be coming to dry the clothes for the wedding.

"Yes, I have," said Halvor. "He has just gone to tear down a spruce tree wood. It won't be long before he's here." He then asked them about the way to Soria Moria Castle and they told him how to get there.

As he approached the castle he noticed that the place was swarming with people and horses. But Halvor's clothes were so tattered and torn after he had followed the west wind through thickets and copses that he remained in the back-ground and kept out of sight until the time came for the bridal feast.

As was the custom, the time came to drink to the bride and

for the cup-bearer to call for a toast to the good health of everyone there, bride and bridegroom, and knights and squires, and last of all the cup was presented to Halvor. As he drank he dropped into the cup the ring which the princess had slipped on to his finger as he lay by the lake, and then asked the cup-bearer to take the cup to the bride with his greetings.

The princess rose from her seat at once and exclaimed, "Who best deserves to have one of us? The one who set us free or the one who sits here as bridegroom?"

Everyone felt that there could be only one answer to that and when Halvor heard that it didn't take him long to get rid of his tattered clothes and dress himself smartly as a bridegroom.

"Yes, yes! That is the right one," exclaimed the youngest princess when she set eyes on him. And so she threw out the other one and was wedded to Halvor.

Soria Moria Castle

About the author:

ROBERT Gambles was born and grew up in Derbyshire. He was a Scholar of St John's College, Oxford, where he took an Honours degree in Modern History and a post-graduate Diploma in Education. He also has a Licentiate Diploma in Music. His professional career was spent in Education, mainly in Cambridge and Liverpool.

He acquired a love of the Lake District early in life and he has lived in Cumbria in his years of retirement during which he has explored the whole district and written a number of books and many articles on various aspects of its history.

Through his Norwegian wife he acquired a special interest in the life and history of Norway.

A keen but pragmatic interest in conservation and the protection of the natural environment has always featured in his philosophy of life and he was for many years a Trustee and member of the Executive Committee of the Friends of the Lake District.

Also by Robert Gambles:

Man in Lakeland: 4,000 years of human settlement
The Story of the Lakeland Dales
Lake District Place Names, published by Hayloft, 2013
Yorkshire Dales Place Names
Out of the Forest: the Natural World and the Place Names of
Cumbria

The Spa resorts and Mineral Springs of Cumbria
Walks on the Borders of Lakeland
Walks around Windermere
Echoes of Old Lakeland
Escape to the Lakes: the first tourists
Great Tales from British History